DAILY

Mood

TRACKER JOURNAL

D1295210

THIS NOTEBOOK BELONGS TO:

NAME:

ADDRESS:

PHONE:

EMAIL:

MONTHLY MOODS TRACKER

	J	F	M	A	M	J	J	A	S	O	N	D
1												
2												
3												
4												
5												
6												
7												
8												
9												
10												
11												
12												
13												
14												
15												
16												
17												
18												
19												
20												
21												
22												
23												
24												
25												
26												
27												
28												
29												
30												
31												

CHOOSE A COLOR FOR EACH
MOOD OR EMOTION.
COLOR IN EACH BOX WITH
THE COLOR OF YOUR
MAIN MOOD THAT DAY.
THIS CAN HELP IDENTIFY PATTERNS.

☐ AMAZING

☐ HAPPY

☐ AVERAGE

☐ SAD

☐ EMOTIONAL

☐ RELAXED

☐ STRESSED

☐ DEPRESSED

☐ EXHAUSTED

☐ BORED

☐ SICK

NOTES

_____
_____
_____
_____
_____
_____
_____
_____
_____

Daily Mood Tracker

DATE: _____

DAY: M – T – W – T – F – S – S

HOURS SLEPT	ENERGY LEVEL	STRESS LEVEL

TODAY I FELT

- loved
- valued
- proud
- grateful

- happy
- joyful
- content
- relaxed

- sick
- tired
- bored
- lazy

- angry
- anxious
- frustrated
- annoyed

- sad
- lonely
- depressed
- insecure

- productive
- motivated
- alive
- excited

- average
- normal
- fine
- OK

THREE THINGS TODAY I AM GRATEFUL FOR

1. _____
2. _____
3. _____

Water Intake (8 Glass A day):

DID I HAVE ENOUGH?   YES   NO

fruits/veggies   ☐   ☐

vitamins   ☐   ☐

fresh air   ☐   ☐

exercise   ☐   ☐

sleep   ☐   ☐

HOW DID I FEEL TODAY IN THE... (CIRCLE ONE)

Morning?

Afternoon?

Evening?

MEDICATIONS

WHAT I DID TO TAKE CARE OF MYSELF

- walk
- meditate
- bath
- cook

- workout
- yoga
- music
- tv/movie

- read
- pets
- drive
- journal

- family
- friends
- play games
- shopping

- do hobbies
- extra sleep
- favourite food
- _____

- _____
- _____
- _____
- _____

What went well? What made me feel good? What I am proud of?

1. _____
2. _____
3. _____

What contributed to negative emotions? What would I change?

1. _____
2. _____
3. _____

Daily Mood Tracker

DATE: _____

DAY: M - T - W - T - F - S - S

HOURS SLEPT

ENERGY LEVEL

STRESS LEVEL

TODAY I FELT

- loved
- valued
- proud
- grateful

- happy
- joyful
- content
- relaxed

- sick
- tired
- bored
- lazy

- angry
- anxious
- frustrated
- annoyed

- sad
- lonely
- depressed
- insecure

- productive
- motivated
- alive
- excited

- average
- normal
- fine
- OK

THREE THINGS TODAY I AM GRATEFUL FOR

1. _____
2. _____
3. _____

Water Intake (8 Glass A day):

DID I HAVE ENOUGH?   YES   NO

fruits/veggies   ☐   ☐

vitamins   ☐   ☐

fresh air   ☐   ☐

exercise   ☐   ☐

sleep   ☐   ☐

HOW DID I FEEL TODAY IN THE... (CIRCLE ONE)

Morning?

Afternoon?

Evening?

MEDICATIONS

WHAT I DID TO TAKE CARE OF MYSELF

- walk
- meditate
- bath
- cook

- workout
- yoga
- music
- tv/movie

- read
- pets
- drive
- journal

- family
- friends
- play games
- shopping

- do hobbies
- extra sleep
- favourite food
- _____

- _____
- _____
- _____
- _____

What went well? What made me feel good? What I am proud of?

1. _____
2. _____
3. _____

What contributed to negative emotions? What would I change?

1. _____
2. _____
3. _____

Daily Mood Tracker

DATE: _____   DAY: M – T – W – T – F – S – S

HOURS SLEPT	ENERGY LEVEL	STRESS LEVEL
	⚡⚡⚡⚡⚡⚡⚡	🧠🧠🧠🧠🧠🧠🧠🧠

TODAY I FELT

- loved
- valued
- proud
- grateful

- happy
- joyful
- content
- relaxed

- sick
- tired
- bored
- lazy

- angry
- anxious
- frustrated
- annoyed

- sad
- lonely
- depressed
- insecure

- productive
- motivated
- alive
- excited

- average
- normal
- fine
- OK

THREE THINGS TODAY I AM GRATEFUL FOR

1. _____
2. _____
3. _____

Water Intake (8 Glass A day):

🥛🥛🥛🥛🥛🥛🥛🥛

DID I HAVE ENOUGH?	YES	NO
fruits/veggies	☐	☐
vitamins	☐	☐
fresh air	☐	☐
exercise	☐	☐
sleep	☐	☐

HOW DID I FEEL TODAY IN THE... (CIRCLE ONE)

Morning? 😊 😁 😎 😐 😴 😵 😠
Afternoon? 😊 😁 😎 😐 😴 😵 😠
Evening? 😊 😁 😎 😐 😴 😵 😠

MEDICATIONS

WHAT I DID TO TAKE CARE OF MYSELF

- walk
- meditate
- bath
- cook

- workout
- yoga
- music
- tv/movie

- read
- pets
- drive
- journal

- family
- friends
- play games
- shopping

- do hobbies
- extra sleep
- favourite food
- _____

- _____
- _____
- _____
- _____

What went well? What made me feel good? What I am proud of?

1. _____
2. _____
3. _____

What contributed to negative emotions? What would I change?

1. _____
2. _____
3. _____

Daily Mood Tracker

DATE: _____

DAY: M – T – W – T – F – S – S

HOURS SLEPT

ENERGY LEVEL

STRESS LEVEL

TODAY I FELT

- loved
- valued
- proud
- grateful

- happy
- joyful
- content
- relaxed

- sick
- tired
- bored
- lazy

- angry
- anxious
- frustrated
- annoyed

- sad
- lonely
- depressed
- insecure

- productive
- motivated
- alive
- excited

- average
- normal
- fine
- OK

THREE THINGS TODAY I AM GRATEFUL FOR

1. _____
2. _____
3. _____

Water Intake (8 Glass A day):

HOW DID I FEEL TODAY IN THE... (CIRCLE ONE)

Morning?

Afternoon?

Evening?

DID I HAVE ENOUGH?

	YES	NO
fruits/veggies	☐	☐
vitamins	☐	☐
fresh air	☐	☐
exercise	☐	☐
sleep	☐	☐

MEDICATIONS

WHAT I DID TO TAKE CARE OF MYSELF

- walk
- meditate
- bath
- cook

- workout
- yoga
- music
- tv/movie

- read
- pets
- drive
- journal

- family
- friends
- play games
- shopping

- do hobbies
- extra sleep
- favourite food

- _____
- _____
- _____
- _____

What went well? What made me feel good? What I am proud of?

1. _____
2. _____
3. _____

What contributed to negative emotions? What would I change?

1. _____
2. _____
3. _____

Daily Mood Tracker

DATE: _____

DAY: M – T – W – T – F – S – S

HOURS SLEPT

ENERGY LEVEL

STRESS LEVEL

TODAY I FELT

- loved
- valued
- proud
- grateful

- happy
- joyful
- content
- relaxed

- sick
- tired
- bored
- lazy

- angry
- anxious
- frustrated
- annoyed

- sad
- lonely
- depressed
- insecure

- productive
- motivated
- alive
- excited

- average
- normal
- fine
- OK

THREE THINGS TODAY I AM GRATEFUL FOR

1. _____
2. _____
3. _____

Water Intake (8 Glass A day):

HOW DID I FEEL TODAY IN THE... (CIRCLE ONE)

Morning?

Afternoon?

Evening?

DID I HAVE ENOUGH?   YES   NO

fruits/veggies   ☐   ☐

vitamins   ☐   ☐

fresh air   ☐   ☐

exercise   ☐   ☐

sleep   ☐   ☐

MEDICATIONS

WHAT I DID TO TAKE CARE OF MYSELF

- walk
- meditate
- bath
- cook

- workout
- yoga
- music
- tv/movie

- read
- pets
- drive
- journal

- family
- friends
- play games
- shopping

- do hobbies
- extra sleep
- favourite food
- _____

- _____
- _____
- _____
- _____

What went well? What made me feel good? What I am proud of?

1. _____
2. _____
3. _____

What contributed to negative emotions? What would I change?

1. _____
2. _____
3. _____

Daily Mood Tracker

DATE: _____   DAY: M – T – W – T – F – S – S

HOURS SLEPT	ENERGY LEVEL	STRESS LEVEL

TODAY I FELT

- loved
- valued
- proud
- grateful

- happy
- joyful
- content
- relaxed

- sick
- tired
- bored
- lazy

- angry
- anxious
- frustrated
- annoyed

- sad
- lonely
- depressed
- insecure

- productive
- motivated
- alive
- excited

- average
- normal
- fine
- OK

THREE THINGS TODAY I AM GRATEFUL FOR

1. _____
2. _____
3. _____

Water Intake (8 Glass A day):

DID I HAVE ENOUGH?   YES   NO

fruits/veggies   ☐   ☐

vitamins   ☐   ☐

fresh air   ☐   ☐

exercise   ☐   ☐

sleep   ☐   ☐

HOW DID I FEEL TODAY IN THE... (CIRCLE ONE)

Morning?

Afternoon?

Evening?

MEDICATIONS

WHAT I DID TO TAKE CARE OF MYSELF

- walk
- meditate
- bath
- cook

- workout
- yoga
- music
- tv/movie

- read
- pets
- drive
- journal

- family
- friends
- play games
- shopping

- do hobbies
- extra sleep
- favourite food
- _____

- _____
- _____
- _____
- _____

What went well? What made me feel good? What I am proud of?

1. _____
2. _____
3. _____

What contributed to negative emotions? What would I change?

1. _____
2. _____
3. _____

Daily Mood Tracker

DATE: _____   DAY: M - T - W - T - F - S - S

HOURS SLEPT

ENERGY LEVEL

STRESS LEVEL

TODAY I FELT

- loved
- valued
- proud
- grateful

- happy
- joyful
- content
- relaxed

- sick
- tired
- bored
- lazy

- angry
- anxious
- frustrated
- annoyed

- sad
- lonely
- depressed
- insecure

- productive
- motivated
- alive
- excited

- average
- normal
- fine
- OK

THREE THINGS TODAY I AM GRATEFUL FOR

1. _____
2. _____
3. _____

Water Intake (8 Glass A day):

HOW DID I FEEL TODAY IN THE... (CIRCLE ONE)

Morning?

Afternoon?

Evening?

DID I HAVE ENOUGH?   YES   NO

fruits/veggies   ☐   ☐

vitamins   ☐   ☐

fresh air   ☐   ☐

exercise   ☐   ☐

sleep   ☐   ☐

MEDICATIONS

WHAT I DID TO TAKE CARE OF MYSELF

- walk
- meditate
- bath
- cook

- workout
- yoga
- music
- tv/movie

- read
- pets
- drive
- journal

- family
- friends
- play games
- shopping

- do hobbies
- extra sleep
- favourite food
- _____

- _____
- _____
- _____
- _____

What went well? What made me feel good? What I am proud of?

1. _____
2. _____
3. _____

What contributed to negative emotions? What would I change?

1. _____
2. _____
3. _____

Daily Mood Tracker

DATE: _____

DAY: M – T – W – T – F – S – S

HOURS SLEPT	ENERGY LEVEL	STRESS LEVEL

TODAY I FELT

- loved
- valued
- proud
- grateful

- happy
- joyful
- content
- relaxed

- sick
- tired
- bored
- lazy

- angry
- anxious
- frustrated
- annoyed

- sad
- lonely
- depressed
- insecure

- productive
- motivated
- alive
- excited

- average
- normal
- fine
- OK

THREE THINGS TODAY I AM GRATEFUL FOR

1. _____
2. _____
3. _____

Water Intake (8 Glass A day):

DID I HAVE ENOUGH?	YES	NO
fruits/veggies	☐	☐
vitamins	☐	☐
fresh air	☐	☐
exercise	☐	☐
sleep	☐	☐

HOW DID I FEEL TODAY IN THE... (CIRCLE ONE)

Morning?

Afternoon?

Evening?

MEDICATIONS

WHAT I DID TO TAKE CARE OF MYSELF

- walk
- meditate
- bath
- cook

- workout
- yoga
- music
- tv/movie

- read
- pets
- drive
- journal

- family
- friends
- play games
- shopping

- do hobbies
- extra sleep
- favourite food

- _____
- _____
- _____
- _____

What went well? What made me feel good? What I am proud of?

1. _____
2. _____
3. _____

What contributed to negative emotions? What would I change?

1. _____
2. _____
3. _____

Daily Mood Tracker

DATE: _____

DAY: M – T – W – T – F – S – S

HOURS SLEPT	ENERGY LEVEL	STRESS LEVEL

TODAY I FELT

- loved
- valued
- proud
- grateful

- happy
- joyful
- content
- relaxed

- sick
- tired
- bored
- lazy

- angry
- anxious
- frustrated
- annoyed

- sad
- lonely
- depressed
- insecure

- productive
- motivated
- alive
- excited

- average
- normal
- fine
- OK

THREE THINGS TODAY I AM GRATEFUL FOR

1. _____
2. _____
3. _____

Water Intake (8 Glass A day):

DID I HAVE ENOUGH?   YES   NO

fruits/veggies   ☐   ☐

vitamins   ☐   ☐

fresh air   ☐   ☐

exercise   ☐   ☐

sleep   ☐   ☐

HOW DID I FEEL TODAY IN THE... (CIRCLE ONE)

Morning?

Afternoon?

Evening?

MEDICATIONS

WHAT I DID TO TAKE CARE OF MYSELF

- walk
- meditate
- bath
- cook

- workout
- yoga
- music
- tv/movie

- read
- pets
- drive
- journal

- family
- friends
- play games
- shopping

- do hobbies
- extra sleep
- favourite food
- _____

- _____
- _____
- _____
- _____

What went well? What made me feel good? What I am proud of?

1. _____
2. _____
3. _____

What contributed to negative emotions? What would I change?

1. _____
2. _____
3. _____

Daily Mood Tracker

DATE: _____

DAY: M – T – W – T – F – S – S

HOURS SLEPT	ENERGY LEVEL	STRESS LEVEL

TODAY I FELT

- loved
- valued
- proud
- grateful

- happy
- joyful
- content
- relaxed

- sick
- tired
- bored
- lazy

- angry
- anxious
- frustrated
- annoyed

- sad
- lonely
- depressed
- insecure

- productive
- motivated
- alive
- excited

- average
- normal
- fine
- OK

THREE THINGS TODAY I AM GRATEFUL FOR

1. _____
2. _____
3. _____

Water Intake (8 Glass A day):

DID I HAVE ENOUGH?   YES   NO

fruits/veggies   ☐   ☐

vitamins   ☐   ☐

fresh air   ☐   ☐

exercise   ☐   ☐

sleep   ☐   ☐

HOW DID I FEEL TODAY IN THE... (CIRCLE ONE)

Morning?

Afternoon?

Evening?

MEDICATIONS

WHAT I DID TO TAKE CARE OF MYSELF

- walk
- meditate
- bath
- cook

- workout
- yoga
- music
- tv/movie

- read
- pets
- drive
- journal

- family
- friends
- play games
- shopping

- do hobbies
- extra sleep
- favourite food
- _____

- _____
- _____
- _____
- _____

What went well? What made me feel good? What I am proud of?

1. _____
2. _____
3. _____

What contributed to negative emotions? What would I change?

1. _____
2. _____
3. _____

Daily Mood Tracker

DATE: _____

DAY: M – T – W – T – F – S – S

HOURS SLEPT

ENERGY LEVEL

STRESS LEVEL

TODAY I FELT

- loved
- valued
- proud
- grateful

- happy
- joyful
- content
- relaxed

- sick
- tired
- bored
- lazy

- angry
- anxious
- frustrated
- annoyed

- sad
- lonely
- depressed
- insecure

- productive
- motivated
- alive
- excited

- average
- normal
- fine
- OK

THREE THINGS TODAY I AM GRATEFUL FOR

1. _____
2. _____
3. _____

Water Intake (8 Glass A day):

HOW DID I FEEL TODAY IN THE... (CIRCLE ONE)

Morning?

Afternoon?

Evening?

DID I HAVE ENOUGH?

	YES	NO
fruits/veggies	☐	☐
vitamins	☐	☐
fresh air	☐	☐
exercise	☐	☐
sleep	☐	☐

MEDICATIONS

WHAT I DID TO TAKE CARE OF MYSELF

- walk
- meditate
- bath
- cook

- workout
- yoga
- music
- tv/movie

- read
- pets
- drive
- journal

- family
- friends
- play games
- shopping

- do hobbies
- extra sleep
- favourite food
- _____

- _____
- _____
- _____
- _____

What went well? What made me feel good? What I am proud of?

1. _____
2. _____
3. _____

What contributed to negative emotions? What would I change?

1. _____
2. _____
3. _____

Daily Mood Tracker

DATE: _____   DAY: M – T – W – T – F – S – S

HOURS SLEPT	ENERGY LEVEL	STRESS LEVEL

TODAY I FELT

- loved
- valued
- proud
- grateful

- happy
- joyful
- content
- relaxed

- sick
- tired
- bored
- lazy

- angry
- anxious
- frustrated
- annoyed

- sad
- lonely
- depressed
- insecure

- productive
- motivated
- alive
- excited

- average
- normal
- fine
- OK

THREE THINGS TODAY I AM GRATEFUL FOR

1. _____
2. _____
3. _____

Water Intake (8 Glass A day):

DID I HAVE ENOUGH?   YES   NO

fruits/veggies   ☐   ☐

vitamins   ☐   ☐

fresh air   ☐   ☐

exercise   ☐   ☐

sleep   ☐   ☐

HOW DID I FEEL TODAY IN THE... (CIRCLE ONE)

Morning?

Afternoon?

Evening?

MEDICATIONS

WHAT I DID TO TAKE CARE OF MYSELF

- walk
- meditate
- bath
- cook

- workout
- yoga
- music
- tv/movie

- read
- pets
- drive
- journal

- family
- friends
- play games
- shopping

- do hobbies
- extra sleep
- favourite food
- _____

- _____
- _____
- _____
- _____

What went well? What made me feel good? What I am proud of?

1. _____
2. _____
3. _____

What contributed to negative emotions? What would I change?

1. _____
2. _____
3. _____

Daily Mood Tracker

DATE: _____   DAY: M – T – W – T – F – S – S

HOURS SLEPT	ENERGY LEVEL	STRESS LEVEL

TODAY I FELT

- loved
- valued
- proud
- grateful

- happy
- joyful
- content
- relaxed

- sick
- tired
- bored
- lazy

- angry
- anxious
- frustrated
- annoyed

- sad
- lonely
- depressed
- insecure

- productive
- motivated
- alive
- excited

- average
- normal
- fine
- OK

THREE THINGS TODAY I AM GRATEFUL FOR

1. _____
2. _____
3. _____

Water Intake (8 Glass A day):

DID I HAVE ENOUGH?   YES   NO

fruits/veggies   ☐   ☐

vitamins   ☐   ☐

fresh air   ☐   ☐

exercise   ☐   ☐

sleep   ☐   ☐

HOW DID I FEEL TODAY IN THE... (CIRCLE ONE)

Morning?

Afternoon?

Evening?

MEDICATIONS

WHAT I DID TO TAKE CARE OF MYSELF

- walk
- meditate
- bath
- cook

- workout
- yoga
- music
- tv/movie

- read
- pets
- drive
- journal

- family
- friends
- play games
- shopping

- do hobbies
- extra sleep
- favourite food

- _____
- _____
- _____
- _____

What went well? What made me feel good? What I am proud of?

1. _____
2. _____
3. _____

What contributed to negative emotions? What would I change?

1. _____
2. _____
3. _____

Daily Mood Tracker

DATE: _____

DAY: M – T – W – T – F – S – S

HOURS SLEPT	ENERGY LEVEL	STRESS LEVEL

TODAY I FELT

- loved
- valued
- proud
- grateful

- happy
- joyful
- content
- relaxed

- sick
- tired
- bored
- lazy

- angry
- anxious
- frustrated
- annoyed

- sad
- lonely
- depressed
- insecure

- productive
- motivated
- alive
- excited

- average
- normal
- fine
- OK

THREE THINGS TODAY I AM GRATEFUL FOR

1. _____
2. _____
3. _____

Water Intake (8 Glass A day):

HOW DID I FEEL TODAY IN THE... (CIRCLE ONE)

Morning?

Afternoon?

Evening?

DID I HAVE ENOUGH?

	YES	NO
fruits/veggies	☐	☐
vitamins	☐	☐
fresh air	☐	☐
exercise	☐	☐
sleep	☐	☐

MEDICATIONS

WHAT I DID TO TAKE CARE OF MYSELF

- walk
- meditate
- bath
- cook

- workout
- yoga
- music
- tv/movie

- read
- pets
- drive
- journal

- family
- friends
- play games
- shopping

- do hobbies
- extra sleep
- favourite food
- _____

- _____
- _____
- _____
- _____

What went well? What made me feel good? What I am proud of?

1. _____
2. _____
3. _____

What contributed to negative emotions? What would I change?

1. _____
2. _____
3. _____

Daily Mood Tracker

DATE: _____

DAY: M – T – W – T – F – S – S

HOURS SLEPT	ENERGY LEVEL	STRESS LEVEL

TODAY I FELT

- loved
- valued
- proud
- grateful

- happy
- joyful
- content
- relaxed

- sick
- tired
- bored
- lazy

- angry
- anxious
- frustrated
- annoyed

- sad
- lonely
- depressed
- insecure

- productive
- motivated
- alive
- excited

- average
- normal
- fine
- OK

THREE THINGS TODAY I AM GRATEFUL FOR

1. _____
2. _____
3. _____

Water Intake (8 Glass A day):

HOW DID I FEEL TODAY IN THE... (CIRCLE ONE)

Morning?

Afternoon?

Evening?

DID I HAVE ENOUGH?   YES   NO

- fruits/veggies ☐ ☐
- vitamins ☐ ☐
- fresh air ☐ ☐
- exercise ☐ ☐
- sleep ☐ ☐

MEDICATIONS

WHAT I DID TO TAKE CARE OF MYSELF

- walk
- meditate
- bath
- cook

- workout
- yoga
- music
- tv/movie

- read
- pets
- drive
- journal

- family
- friends
- play games
- shopping

- do hobbies
- extra sleep
- favourite food
- _____

- _____
- _____
- _____
- _____

What went well? What made me feel good? What I am proud of?

1. _____
2. _____
3. _____

What contributed to negative emotions? What would I change?

1. _____
2. _____
3. _____

Daily Mood Tracker

DATE: _____

DAY: M – T – W – T – F – S – S

HOURS SLEPT	ENERGY LEVEL	STRESS LEVEL

TODAY I FELT

- loved
- valued
- proud
- grateful

- happy
- joyful
- content
- relaxed

- sick
- tired
- bored
- lazy

- angry
- anxious
- frustrated
- annoyed

- sad
- lonely
- depressed
- insecure

- productive
- motivated
- alive
- excited

- average
- normal
- fine
- OK

THREE THINGS TODAY I AM GRATEFUL FOR

1. _____
2. _____
3. _____

Water Intake (8 Glass A day):

DID I HAVE ENOUGH?   YES   NO

fruits/veggies   ☐   ☐

vitamins   ☐   ☐

fresh air   ☐   ☐

exercise   ☐   ☐

sleep   ☐   ☐

HOW DID I FEEL TODAY IN THE... (CIRCLE ONE)

Morning?

Afternoon?

Evening?

MEDICATIONS

WHAT I DID TO TAKE CARE OF MYSELF

- walk
- meditate
- bath
- cook

- workout
- yoga
- music
- tv/movie

- read
- pets
- drive
- journal

- family
- friends
- play games
- shopping

- do hobbies
- extra sleep
- favourite food
- _____

- _____
- _____
- _____
- _____

What went well? What made me feel good? What I am proud of?

1. _____
2. _____
3. _____

What contributed to negative emotions? What would I change?

1. _____
2. _____
3. _____

Daily Mood Tracker

DATE: _____

DAY: M – T – W – T – F – S – S

HOURS SLEPT	ENERGY LEVEL	STRESS LEVEL

TODAY I FELT

- loved
- valued
- proud
- grateful

- happy
- joyful
- content
- relaxed

- sick
- tired
- bored
- lazy

- angry
- anxious
- frustrated
- annoyed

- sad
- lonely
- depressed
- insecure

- productive
- motivated
- alive
- excited

- average
- normal
- fine
- OK

THREE THINGS TODAY I AM GRATEFUL FOR

1. _____
2. _____
3. _____

Water Intake (8 Glass A day):

DID I HAVE ENOUGH?   YES   NO

fruits/veggies   ☐ ☐

vitamins   ☐ ☐

fresh air   ☐ ☐

exercise   ☐ ☐

sleep   ☐ ☐

HOW DID I FEEL TODAY IN THE... (CIRCLE ONE)

Morning?

Afternoon?

Evening?

MEDICATIONS

WHAT I DID TO TAKE CARE OF MYSELF

- walk
- meditate
- bath
- cook

- workout
- yoga
- music
- tv/movie

- read
- pets
- drive
- journal

- family
- friends
- play games
- shopping

- do hobbies
- extra sleep
- favourite food
- _____

- _____
- _____
- _____
- _____

What went well? What made me feel good? What I am proud of?

1. _____
2. _____
3. _____

What contributed to negative emotions? What would I change?

1. _____
2. _____
3. _____

Daily Mood Tracker

DATE: _____

DAY: M - T - W - T - F - S - S

HOURS SLEPT

ENERGY LEVEL

STRESS LEVEL

TODAY I FELT

- loved
- valued
- proud
- grateful

- happy
- joyful
- content
- relaxed

- sick
- tired
- bored
- lazy

- angry
- anxious
- frustrated
- annoyed

- sad
- lonely
- depressed
- insecure

- productive
- motivated
- alive
- excited

- average
- normal
- fine
- OK

THREE THINGS TODAY I AM GRATEFUL FOR

1. _____
2. _____
3. _____

Water Intake (8 Glass A day):

HOW DID I FEEL TODAY IN THE... (CIRCLE ONE)

Morning?

Afternoon?

Evening?

DID I HAVE ENOUGH?   YES   NO

fruits/veggies   ☐ ☐

vitamins   ☐ ☐

fresh air   ☐ ☐

exercise   ☐ ☐

sleep   ☐ ☐

MEDICATIONS

WHAT I DID TO TAKE CARE OF MYSELF

- walk
- meditate
- bath
- cook

- workout
- yoga
- music
- tv/movie

- read
- pets
- drive
- journal

- family
- friends
- play games
- shopping

- do hobbies
- extra sleep
- favourite food
- _____

- _____
- _____
- _____
- _____

What went well? What made me feel good? What I am proud of?

1. _____
2. _____
3. _____

What contributed to negative emotions? What would I change?

1. _____
2. _____
3. _____

Daily Mood Tracker

DATE: _____

DAY: M – T – W – T – F – S – S

HOURS SLEPT

ENERGY LEVEL

STRESS LEVEL

TODAY I FELT

- loved
- valued
- proud
- grateful

- happy
- joyful
- content
- relaxed

- sick
- tired
- bored
- lazy

- angry
- anxious
- frustrated
- annoyed

- sad
- lonely
- depressed
- insecure

- productive
- motivated
- alive
- excited

- average
- normal
- fine
- OK

THREE THINGS TODAY I AM GRATEFUL FOR

1. _____
2. _____
3. _____

Water Intake (8 Glass A day):

DID I HAVE ENOUGH?   YES   NO

fruits/veggies   ☐   ☐

vitamins   ☐   ☐

fresh air   ☐   ☐

exercise   ☐   ☐

sleep   ☐   ☐

HOW DID I FEEL TODAY IN THE... (CIRCLE ONE)

Morning?

Afternoon?

Evening?

MEDICATIONS

WHAT I DID TO TAKE CARE OF MYSELF

- walk
- meditate
- bath
- cook

- workout
- yoga
- music
- tv/movie

- read
- pets
- drive
- journal

- family
- friends
- play games
- shopping

- do hobbies
- extra sleep
- favourite food
- _____

- _____
- _____
- _____
- _____

What went well? What made me feel good? What I am proud of?

1. _____
2. _____
3. _____

What contributed to negative emotions? What would I change?

1. _____
2. _____
3. _____

Daily Mood Tracker

DATE: _____

DAY: M – T – W – T – F – S – S

HOURS SLEPT	ENERGY LEVEL	STRESS LEVEL

TODAY I FELT

- loved
- valued
- proud
- grateful

- happy
- joyful
- content
- relaxed

- sick
- tired
- bored
- lazy

- angry
- anxious
- frustrated
- annoyed

- sad
- lonely
- depressed
- insecure

- productive
- motivated
- alive
- excited

- average
- normal
- fine
- OK

THREE THINGS TODAY I AM GRATEFUL FOR

1. _____
2. _____
3. _____

Water Intake (8 Glass A day):

HOW DID I FEEL TODAY IN THE... (CIRCLE ONE)

Morning?

Afternoon?

Evening?

DID I HAVE ENOUGH?	YES	NO
fruits/veggies	☐	☐
vitamins	☐	☐
fresh air	☐	☐
exercise	☐	☐
sleep	☐	☐

MEDICATIONS

WHAT I DID TO TAKE CARE OF MYSELF

- walk
- meditate
- bath
- cook

- workout
- yoga
- music
- tv/movie

- read
- pets
- drive
- journal

- family
- friends
- play games
- shopping

- do hobbies
- extra sleep
- favourite food
- _____

- _____
- _____
- _____
- _____

What went well? What made me feel good? What I am proud of?

1. _____
2. _____
3. _____

What contributed to negative emotions? What would I change?

1. _____
2. _____
3. _____

Daily Mood Tracker

DATE: _____

DAY: M – T – W – T – F – S – S

HOURS SLEPT	ENERGY LEVEL	STRESS LEVEL

TODAY I FELT

- loved
- valued
- proud
- grateful

- happy
- joyful
- content
- relaxed

- sick
- tired
- bored
- lazy

- angry
- anxious
- frustrated
- annoyed

- sad
- lonely
- depressed
- insecure

- productive
- motivated
- alive
- excited

- average
- normal
- fine
- OK

THREE THINGS TODAY I AM GRATEFUL FOR

1. _____
2. _____
3. _____

Water Intake (8 Glass A day):

DID I HAVE ENOUGH?

	YES	NO
fruits/veggies	☐	☐
vitamins	☐	☐
fresh air	☐	☐
exercise	☐	☐
sleep	☐	☐

HOW DID I FEEL TODAY IN THE... (CIRCLE ONE)

Morning?

Afternoon?

Evening?

MEDICATIONS

WHAT I DID TO TAKE CARE OF MYSELF

- walk
- meditate
- bath
- cook

- workout
- yoga
- music
- tv/movie

- read
- pets
- drive
- journal

- family
- friends
- play games
- shopping

- do hobbies
- extra sleep
- favourite food
- _____

- _____
- _____
- _____
- _____

What went well? What made me feel good? What I am proud of?

1. _____
2. _____
3. _____

What contributed to negative emotions? What would I change?

1. _____
2. _____
3. _____

Daily Mood Tracker

DATE: _____

DAY: M – T – W – T – F – S – S

HOURS SLEPT	ENERGY LEVEL	STRESS LEVEL

TODAY I FELT

- loved
- valued
- proud
- grateful

- happy
- joyful
- content
- relaxed

- sick
- tired
- bored
- lazy

- angry
- anxious
- frustrated
- annoyed

- sad
- lonely
- depressed
- insecure

- productive
- motivated
- alive
- excited

- average
- normal
- fine
- OK

THREE THINGS TODAY I AM GRATEFUL FOR

1. _____
2. _____
3. _____

Water Intake (8 Glass A day):

HOW DID I FEEL TODAY IN THE... (CIRCLE ONE)

Morning?

Afternoon?

Evening?

DID I HAVE ENOUGH?

	YES	NO
fruits/veggies	☐	☐
vitamins	☐	☐
fresh air	☐	☐
exercise	☐	☐
sleep	☐	☐

MEDICATIONS

WHAT I DID TO TAKE CARE OF MYSELF

- walk
- meditate
- bath
- cook

- workout
- yoga
- music
- tv/movie

- read
- pets
- drive
- journal

- family
- friends
- play games
- shopping

- do hobbies
- extra sleep
- favourite food
- _____

- _____
- _____
- _____
- _____

What went well? What made me feel good? What I am proud of?

1. _____
2. _____
3. _____

What contributed to negative emotions? What would I change?

1. _____
2. _____
3. _____

Daily Mood Tracker

DATE: _____   DAY: M – T – W – T – F – S – S

HOURS SLEPT

ENERGY LEVEL

STRESS LEVEL

TODAY I FELT

- loved
- valued
- proud
- grateful

- happy
- joyful
- content
- relaxed

- sick
- tired
- bored
- lazy

- angry
- anxious
- frustrated
- annoyed

- sad
- lonely
- depressed
- insecure

- productive
- motivated
- alive
- excited

- average
- normal
- fine
- OK

THREE THINGS TODAY I AM GRATEFUL FOR

1. _____
2. _____
3. _____

Water Intake (8 Glass A day):

DID I HAVE ENOUGH?   YES   NO

fruits/veggies   ☐   ☐

vitamins   ☐   ☐

fresh air   ☐   ☐

exercise   ☐   ☐

sleep   ☐   ☐

HOW DID I FEEL TODAY IN THE... (CIRCLE ONE)

Morning?

Afternoon?

Evening?

MEDICATIONS

WHAT I DID TO TAKE CARE OF MYSELF

- walk
- meditate
- bath
- cook

- workout
- yoga
- music
- tv/movie

- read
- pets
- drive
- journal

- family
- friends
- play games
- shopping

- do hobbies
- extra sleep
- favourite food
- _____

- _____
- _____
- _____
- _____

What went well? What made me feel good? What I am proud of?

1. _____
2. _____
3. _____

What contributed to negative emotions? What would I change?

1. _____
2. _____
3. _____

Daily Mood Tracker

DATE: _____   DAY: M – T – W – T – F – S – S

HOURS SLEPT	ENERGY LEVEL	STRESS LEVEL

TODAY I FELT

- loved
- valued
- proud
- grateful

- happy
- joyful
- content
- relaxed

- sick
- tired
- bored
- lazy

- angry
- anxious
- frustrated
- annoyed

- sad
- lonely
- depressed
- insecure

- productive
- motivated
- alive
- excited

- average
- normal
- fine
- OK

THREE THINGS TODAY I AM GRATEFUL FOR

1. _____
2. _____
3. _____

Water Intake (8 Glass A day):

DID I HAVE ENOUGH?

	YES	NO
fruits/veggies	☐	☐
vitamins	☐	☐
fresh air	☐	☐
exercise	☐	☐
sleep	☐	☐

HOW DID I FEEL TODAY IN THE... (CIRCLE ONE)

Morning?

Afternoon?

Evening?

MEDICATIONS

WHAT I DID TO TAKE CARE OF MYSELF

- walk
- meditate
- bath
- cook

- workout
- yoga
- music
- tv/movie

- read
- pets
- drive
- journal

- family
- friends
- play games
- shopping

- do hobbies
- extra sleep
- favourite food
- _____

- _____
- _____
- _____
- _____

What went well? What made me feel good? What I am proud of?

1. _____
2. _____
3. _____

What contributed to negative emotions? What would I change?

1. _____
2. _____
3. _____

Daily Mood Tracker

DATE: _____

DAY: M – T – W – T – F – S – S

HOURS SLEPT	ENERGY LEVEL	STRESS LEVEL

TODAY I FELT

- loved
- valued
- proud
- grateful

- happy
- joyful
- content
- relaxed

- sick
- tired
- bored
- lazy

- angry
- anxious
- frustrated
- annoyed

- sad
- lonely
- depressed
- insecure

- productive
- motivated
- alive
- excited

- average
- normal
- fine
- OK

THREE THINGS TODAY I AM GRATEFUL FOR

1. _____
2. _____
3. _____

Water Intake (8 Glass A day):

DID I HAVE ENOUGH?   YES   NO

fruits/veggies   ☐   ☐

vitamins   ☐   ☐

fresh air   ☐   ☐

exercise   ☐   ☐

sleep   ☐   ☐

HOW DID I FEEL TODAY IN THE... (CIRCLE ONE)

Morning?

Afternoon?

Evening?

MEDICATIONS

WHAT I DID TO TAKE CARE OF MYSELF

- walk
- meditate
- bath
- cook

- workout
- yoga
- music
- tv/movie

- read
- pets
- drive
- journal

- family
- friends
- play games
- shopping

- do hobbies
- extra sleep
- favourite food
- _____

- _____
- _____
- _____
- _____

What went well? What made me feel good? What I am proud of?

1. _____
2. _____
3. _____

What contributed to negative emotions? What would I change?

1. _____
2. _____
3. _____

Daily Mood Tracker

DATE: _____

DAY: M - T - W - T - F - S - S

HOURS SLEPT	ENERGY LEVEL	STRESS LEVEL

TODAY I FELT

- loved
- valued
- proud
- grateful

- happy
- joyful
- content
- relaxed

- sick
- tired
- bored
- lazy

- angry
- anxious
- frustrated
- annoyed

- sad
- lonely
- depressed
- insecure

- productive
- motivated
- alive
- excited

- average
- normal
- fine
- OK

THREE THINGS TODAY I AM GRATEFUL FOR

1. _____
2. _____
3. _____

Water Intake (8 Glass A day):

HOW DID I FEEL TODAY IN THE... (CIRCLE ONE)

Morning?

Afternoon?

Evening?

DID I HAVE ENOUGH?

	YES	NO
fruits/veggies	☐	☐
vitamins	☐	☐
fresh air	☐	☐
exercise	☐	☐
sleep	☐	☐

MEDICATIONS

WHAT I DID TO TAKE CARE OF MYSELF

- walk
- meditate
- bath
- cook

- workout
- yoga
- music
- tv/movie

- read
- pets
- drive
- journal

- family
- friends
- play games
- shopping

- do hobbies
- extra sleep
- favourite food
-

- _____
- _____
- _____
- _____

What went well? What made me feel good? What I am proud of?

1. _____
2. _____
3. _____

What contributed to negative emotions? What would I change?

1. _____
2. _____
3. _____

Daily Mood Tracker

DATE: _____

DAY: M – T – W – T – F – S – S

HOURS SLEPT	ENERGY LEVEL	STRESS LEVEL

TODAY I FELT

• loved	• happy	• sick	• angry	• sad	• productive	• average
• valued	• joyful	• tired	• anxious	• lonely	• motivated	• normal
• proud	• content	• bored	• frustrated	• depressed	• alive	• fine
• grateful	• relaxed	• lazy	• annoyed	• insecure	• excited	• OK

THREE THINGS TODAY I AM GRATEFUL FOR

1. _____
2. _____
3. _____

Water Intake (8 Glass A day):

DID I HAVE ENOUGH?   YES   NO

fruits/veggies   ☐   ☐

vitamins   ☐   ☐

fresh air   ☐   ☐

exercise   ☐   ☐

sleep   ☐   ☐

HOW DID I FEEL TODAY IN THE... (CIRCLE ONE)

Morning?

Afternoon?

Evening?

MEDICATIONS

WHAT I DID TO TAKE CARE OF MYSELF

• walk	• workout	• read	• family	• do hobbies	• _____
• meditate	• yoga	• pets	• friends	• extra sleep	• _____
• bath	• music	• drive	• play games	• favourite food	• _____
• cook	• tv/movie	• journal	• shopping	• _____	• _____

What went well? What made me feel good? What I am proud of?

1. _____
2. _____
3. _____

What contributed to negative emotions? What would I change?

1. _____
2. _____
3. _____

Daily Mood Tracker

DATE: _____

DAY: M – T – W – T – F – S – S

HOURS SLEPT	ENERGY LEVEL	STRESS LEVEL

TODAY I FELT

- loved
- valued
- proud
- grateful

- happy
- joyful
- content
- relaxed

- sick
- tired
- bored
- lazy

- angry
- anxious
- frustrated
- annoyed

- sad
- lonely
- depressed
- insecure

- productive
- motivated
- alive
- excited

- average
- normal
- fine
- OK

THREE THINGS TODAY I AM GRATEFUL FOR

1. _____
2. _____
3. _____

Water Intake (8 Glass A day):

DID I HAVE ENOUGH?   YES   NO

- fruits/veggies   ☐   ☐
- vitamins   ☐   ☐
- fresh air   ☐   ☐
- exercise   ☐   ☐
- sleep   ☐   ☐

HOW DID I FEEL TODAY IN THE... (CIRCLE ONE)

Morning?

Afternoon?

Evening?

MEDICATIONS

WHAT I DID TO TAKE CARE OF MYSELF

- walk
- meditate
- bath
- cook

- workout
- yoga
- music
- tv/movie

- read
- pets
- drive
- journal

- family
- friends
- play games
- shopping

- do hobbies
- extra sleep
- favourite food
- _____

- _____
- _____
- _____
- _____

What went well? What made me feel good? What I am proud of?

1. _____
2. _____
3. _____

What contributed to negative emotions? What would I change?

1. _____
2. _____
3. _____

Daily Mood Tracker

DATE: _____

DAY: M – T – W – T – F – S – S

HOURS SLEPT

ENERGY LEVEL

STRESS LEVEL

TODAY I FELT

- loved
- valued
- proud
- grateful

- happy
- joyful
- content
- relaxed

- sick
- tired
- bored
- lazy

- angry
- anxious
- frustrated
- annoyed

- sad
- lonely
- depressed
- insecure

- productive
- motivated
- alive
- excited

- average
- normal
- fine
- OK

THREE THINGS TODAY I AM GRATEFUL FOR

1. _____
2. _____
3. _____

Water Intake (8 Glass A day):

HOW DID I FEEL TODAY IN THE... (CIRCLE ONE)

Morning?

Afternoon?

Evening?

DID I HAVE ENOUGH?   YES   NO

fruits/veggies   ☐   ☐

vitamins   ☐   ☐

fresh air   ☐   ☐

exercise   ☐   ☐

sleep   ☐   ☐

MEDICATIONS

WHAT I DID TO TAKE CARE OF MYSELF

- walk
- meditate
- bath
- cook

- workout
- yoga
- music
- tv/movie

- read
- pets
- drive
- journal

- family
- friends
- play games
- shopping

- do hobbies
- extra sleep
- favourite food
-

- _____
- _____
- _____
- _____

What went well? What made me feel good? What I am proud of?

1. _____
2. _____
3. _____

What contributed to negative emotions? What would I change?

1. _____
2. _____
3. _____

Daily Mood Tracker

DATE: _____

DAY: M – T – W – T – F – S – S

HOURS SLEPT

ENERGY LEVEL

STRESS LEVEL

TODAY I FELT

- loved
- valued
- proud
- grateful

- happy
- joyful
- content
- relaxed

- sick
- tired
- bored
- lazy

- angry
- anxious
- frustrated
- annoyed

- sad
- lonely
- depressed
- insecure

- productive
- motivated
- alive
- excited

- average
- normal
- fine
- OK

THREE THINGS TODAY I AM GRATEFUL FOR

1. _____
2. _____
3. _____

Water Intake (8 Glass A day):

DID I HAVE ENOUGH?   YES   NO

fruits/veggies   ☐   ☐

vitamins   ☐   ☐

fresh air   ☐   ☐

exercise   ☐   ☐

sleep   ☐   ☐

HOW DID I FEEL TODAY IN THE... (CIRCLE ONE)

Morning?

Afternoon?

Evening?

MEDICATIONS

WHAT I DID TO TAKE CARE OF MYSELF

- walk
- meditate
- bath
- cook

- workout
- yoga
- music
- tv/movie

- read
- pets
- drive
- journal

- family
- friends
- play games
- shopping

- do hobbies
- extra sleep
- favourite food
- _____

- _____
- _____
- _____
- _____

What went well? What made me feel good? What I am proud of?

1. _____
2. _____
3. _____

What contributed to negative emotions? What would I change?

1. _____
2. _____
3. _____

Daily Mood Tracker

DATE: _____   DAY: M – T – W – T – F – S – S

HOURS SLEPT	ENERGY LEVEL	STRESS LEVEL

TODAY I FELT

• loved	• happy	• sick	• angry	• sad	• productive	• average
• valued	• joyful	• tired	• anxious	• lonely	• motivated	• normal
• proud	• content	• bored	• frustrated	• depressed	• alive	• fine
• grateful	• relaxed	• lazy	• annoyed	• insecure	• excited	• OK

THREE THINGS TODAY I AM GRATEFUL FOR

1. _____
2. _____
3. _____

Water Intake (8 Glass A day):

DID I HAVE ENOUGH?   YES   NO

	YES	NO
fruits/veggies	☐	☐
vitamins	☐	☐
fresh air	☐	☐
exercise	☐	☐
sleep	☐	☐

HOW DID I FEEL TODAY IN THE... (CIRCLE ONE)

Morning?

Afternoon?

Evening?

MEDICATIONS

WHAT I DID TO TAKE CARE OF MYSELF

• walk	• workout	• read	• family	• do hobbies	• _____
• meditate	• yoga	• pets	• friends	• extra sleep	• _____
• bath	• music	• drive	• play games	• favourite food	• _____
• cook	• tv/movie	• journal	• shopping	• _____	• _____

What went well? What made me feel good? What I am proud of?

1. _____
2. _____
3. _____

What contributed to negative emotions? What would I change?

1. _____
2. _____
3. _____

Daily Mood Tracker

DATE: _____

DAY: M – T – W – T – F – S – S

HOURS SLEPT	ENERGY LEVEL	STRESS LEVEL

TODAY I FELT

- loved
- valued
- proud
- grateful

- happy
- joyful
- content
- relaxed

- sick
- tired
- bored
- lazy

- angry
- anxious
- frustrated
- annoyed

- sad
- lonely
- depressed
- insecure

- productive
- motivated
- alive
- excited

- average
- normal
- fine
- OK

THREE THINGS TODAY I AM GRATEFUL FOR

1. _____
2. _____
3. _____

Water Intake (8 Glass A day):

HOW DID I FEEL TODAY IN THE... (CIRCLE ONE)

Morning?

Afternoon?

Evening?

DID I HAVE ENOUGH?   YES   NO

fruits/veggies ☐ ☐

vitamins ☐ ☐

fresh air ☐ ☐

exercise ☐ ☐

sleep ☐ ☐

MEDICATIONS

WHAT I DID TO TAKE CARE OF MYSELF

- walk
- meditate
- bath
- cook

- workout
- yoga
- music
- tv/movie

- read
- pets
- drive
- journal

- family
- friends
- play games
- shopping

- do hobbies
- extra sleep
- favourite food
- _____

- _____
- _____
- _____
- _____

What went well? What made me feel good? What I am proud of?

1. _____
2. _____
3. _____

What contributed to negative emotions? What would I change?

1. _____
2. _____
3. _____

Daily Mood Tracker

DATE: _____

DAY: M – T – W – T – F – S – S

HOURS SLEPT

ENERGY LEVEL

STRESS LEVEL

TODAY I FELT

- loved
- valued
- proud
- grateful

- happy
- joyful
- content
- relaxed

- sick
- tired
- bored
- lazy

- angry
- anxious
- frustrated
- annoyed

- sad
- lonely
- depressed
- insecure

- productive
- motivated
- alive
- excited

- average
- normal
- fine
- OK

THREE THINGS TODAY I AM GRATEFUL FOR

1. _____
2. _____
3. _____

Water Intake (8 Glass A day):

HOW DID I FEEL TODAY IN THE... (CIRCLE ONE)

Morning?

Afternoon?

Evening?

DID I HAVE ENOUGH?	YES	NO
fruits/veggies	☐	☐
vitamins	☐	☐
fresh air	☐	☐
exercise	☐	☐
sleep	☐	☐

MEDICATIONS

WHAT I DID TO TAKE CARE OF MYSELF

- walk
- meditate
- bath
- cook

- workout
- yoga
- music
- tv/movie

- read
- pets
- drive
- journal

- family
- friends
- play games
- shopping

- do hobbies
- extra sleep
- favourite food
- _____

- _____
- _____
- _____
- _____

What went well? What made me feel good? What I am proud of?

1. _____
2. _____
3. _____

What contributed to negative emotions? What would I change?

1. _____
2. _____
3. _____

Daily Mood Tracker

DATE: _____

DAY: M – T – W – T – F – S – S

HOURS SLEPT	ENERGY LEVEL	STRESS LEVEL

TODAY I FELT

- loved
- valued
- proud
- grateful

- happy
- joyful
- content
- relaxed

- sick
- tired
- bored
- lazy

- angry
- anxious
- frustrated
- annoyed

- sad
- lonely
- depressed
- insecure

- productive
- motivated
- alive
- excited

- average
- normal
- fine
- OK

THREE THINGS TODAY I AM GRATEFUL FOR

1. _____
2. _____
3. _____

Water Intake (8 Glass A day):

HOW DID I FEEL TODAY IN THE... (CIRCLE ONE)

Morning?

Afternoon?

Evening?

DID I HAVE ENOUGH?	YES	NO
fruits/veggies	☐	☐
vitamins	☐	☐
fresh air	☐	☐
exercise	☐	☐
sleep	☐	☐

MEDICATIONS

WHAT I DID TO TAKE CARE OF MYSELF

- walk
- meditate
- bath
- cook

- workout
- yoga
- music
- tv/movie

- read
- pets
- drive
- journal

- family
- friends
- play games
- shopping

- do hobbies
- extra sleep
- favourite food
- _____

- _____
- _____
- _____
- _____

What went well? What made me feel good? What I am proud of?

1. _____
2. _____
3. _____

What contributed to negative emotions? What would I change?

1. _____
2. _____
3. _____

Daily Mood Tracker

DATE: _____   DAY: M – T – W – T – F – S – S

HOURS SLEPT	ENERGY LEVEL	STRESS LEVEL

TODAY I FELT

- loved
- valued
- proud
- grateful

- happy
- joyful
- content
- relaxed

- sick
- tired
- bored
- lazy

- angry
- anxious
- frustrated
- annoyed

- sad
- lonely
- depressed
- insecure

- productive
- motivated
- alive
- excited

- average
- normal
- fine
- OK

THREE THINGS TODAY I AM GRATEFUL FOR

1. _____
2. _____
3. _____

Water Intake (8 Glass A day):

HOW DID I FEEL TODAY IN THE... (CIRCLE ONE)

Morning?

Afternoon?

Evening?

DID I HAVE ENOUGH?   YES   NO

fruits/veggies   ☐   ☐

vitamins   ☐   ☐

fresh air   ☐   ☐

exercise   ☐   ☐

sleep   ☐   ☐

MEDICATIONS

WHAT I DID TO TAKE CARE OF MYSELF

- walk
- meditate
- bath
- cook

- workout
- yoga
- music
- tv/movie

- read
- pets
- drive
- journal

- family
- friends
- play games
- shopping

- do hobbies
- extra sleep
- favourite food
- _____

- _____
- _____
- _____
- _____

What went well? What made me feel good? What I am proud of?

1. _____
2. _____
3. _____

What contributed to negative emotions? What would I change?

1. _____
2. _____
3. _____

Daily Mood Tracker

DATE: _____

DAY: M – T – W – T – F – S – S

HOURS SLEPT

ENERGY LEVEL

STRESS LEVEL

TODAY I FELT

- loved
- valued
- proud
- grateful

- happy
- joyful
- content
- relaxed

- sick
- tired
- bored
- lazy

- angry
- anxious
- frustrated
- annoyed

- sad
- lonely
- depressed
- insecure

- productive
- motivated
- alive
- excited

- average
- normal
- fine
- OK

THREE THINGS TODAY I AM GRATEFUL FOR

1. _____
2. _____
3. _____

Water Intake (8 Glass A day):

DID I HAVE ENOUGH?

	YES	NO
fruits/veggies	☐	☐
vitamins	☐	☐
fresh air	☐	☐
exercise	☐	☐
sleep	☐	☐

HOW DID I FEEL TODAY IN THE... (CIRCLE ONE)

Morning?

Afternoon?

Evening?

MEDICATIONS

WHAT I DID TO TAKE CARE OF MYSELF

- walk
- meditate
- bath
- cook

- workout
- yoga
- music
- tv/movie

- read
- pets
- drive
- journal

- family
- friends
- play games
- shopping

- do hobbies
- extra sleep
- favourite food
- _____

- _____
- _____
- _____
- _____

What went well? What made me feel good? What I am proud of?

1. _____
2. _____
3. _____

What contributed to negative emotions? What would I change?

1. _____
2. _____
3. _____

Daily Mood Tracker

DATE: _____   DAY: M – T – W – T – F – S – S

HOURS SLEPT

ENERGY LEVEL

STRESS LEVEL

TODAY I FELT

- loved
- valued
- proud
- grateful

- happy
- joyful
- content
- relaxed

- sick
- tired
- bored
- lazy

- angry
- anxious
- frustrated
- annoyed

- sad
- lonely
- depressed
- insecure

- productive
- motivated
- alive
- excited

- average
- normal
- fine
- OK

THREE THINGS TODAY I AM GRATEFUL FOR

1. _____
2. _____
3. _____

Water Intake (8 Glass A day):

DID I HAVE ENOUGH?   YES   NO

fruits/veggies   ☐   ☐

vitamins   ☐   ☐

fresh air   ☐   ☐

exercise   ☐   ☐

sleep   ☐   ☐

HOW DID I FEEL TODAY IN THE... (CIRCLE ONE)

Morning?

Afternoon?

Evening?

MEDICATIONS

WHAT I DID TO TAKE CARE OF MYSELF

- walk
- meditate
- bath
- cook

- workout
- yoga
- music
- tv/movie

- read
- pets
- drive
- journal

- family
- friends
- play games
- shopping

- do hobbies
- extra sleep
- favourite food
- _____

- _____
- _____
- _____
- _____

What went well? What made me feel good? What I am proud of?

1. _____
2. _____
3. _____

What contributed to negative emotions? What would I change?

1. _____
2. _____
3. _____

Daily Mood Tracker

DATE: _____   DAY: M - T - W - T - F - S - S

HOURS SLEPT	ENERGY LEVEL	STRESS LEVEL

TODAY I FELT

- loved
- valued
- proud
- grateful

- happy
- joyful
- content
- relaxed

- sick
- tired
- bored
- lazy

- angry
- anxious
- frustrated
- annoyed

- sad
- lonely
- depressed
- insecure

- productive
- motivated
- alive
- excited

- average
- normal
- fine
- OK

THREE THINGS TODAY I AM GRATEFUL FOR

1. _____
2. _____
3. _____

Water Intake (8 Glass A day):

DID I HAVE ENOUGH?   YES   NO

fruits/veggies   ☐   ☐
vitamins   ☐   ☐
fresh air   ☐   ☐
exercise   ☐   ☐
sleep   ☐   ☐

HOW DID I FEEL TODAY IN THE... (CIRCLE ONE)

Morning?
Afternoon?
Evening?

MEDICATIONS

WHAT I DID TO TAKE CARE OF MYSELF

- walk
- meditate
- bath
- cook

- workout
- yoga
- music
- tv/movie

- read
- pets
- drive
- journal

- family
- friends
- play games
- shopping

- do hobbies
- extra sleep
- favourite food
- _____

- _____
- _____
- _____

What went well? What made me feel good? What I am proud of?

1. _____
2. _____
3. _____

What contributed to negative emotions? What would I change?

1. _____
2. _____
3. _____

Daily Mood Tracker

DATE: _____   DAY: M - T - W - T - F - S - S

HOURS SLEPT	ENERGY LEVEL	STRESS LEVEL

TODAY I FELT

- loved
- valued
- proud
- grateful

- happy
- joyful
- content
- relaxed

- sick
- tired
- bored
- lazy

- angry
- anxious
- frustrated
- annoyed

- sad
- lonely
- depressed
- insecure

- productive
- motivated
- alive
- excited

- average
- normal
- fine
- OK

THREE THINGS TODAY I AM GRATEFUL FOR

1. _____
2. _____
3. _____

Water Intake (8 Glass A day):

HOW DID I FEEL TODAY IN THE... (CIRCLE ONE)

Morning?
Afternoon?
Evening?

DID I HAVE ENOUGH?   YES   NO

fruits/veggies   ☐   ☐
vitamins   ☐   ☐
fresh air   ☐   ☐
exercise   ☐   ☐
sleep   ☐   ☐

MEDICATIONS

WHAT I DID TO TAKE CARE OF MYSELF

- walk
- meditate
- bath
- cook

- workout
- yoga
- music
- tv/movie

- read
- pets
- drive
- journal

- family
- friends
- play games
- shopping

- do hobbies
- extra sleep
- favourite food
- _____

- _____
- _____
- _____
- _____

What went well? What made me feel good? What I am proud of?

1. _____
2. _____
3. _____

What contributed to negative emotions? What would I change?

1. _____
2. _____
3. _____

Daily Mood Tracker

DATE: _____   DAY: M – T – W – T – F – S – S

HOURS SLEPT	ENERGY LEVEL	STRESS LEVEL

TODAY I FELT

- loved
- valued
- proud
- grateful

- happy
- joyful
- content
- relaxed

- sick
- tired
- bored
- lazy

- angry
- anxious
- frustrated
- annoyed

- sad
- lonely
- depressed
- insecure

- productive
- motivated
- alive
- excited

- average
- normal
- fine
- OK

THREE THINGS TODAY I AM GRATEFUL FOR

1. _____
2. _____
3. _____

Water Intake (8 Glass A day):

DID I HAVE ENOUGH?	YES	NO
fruits/veggies	☐	☐
vitamins	☐	☐
fresh air	☐	☐
exercise	☐	☐
sleep	☐	☐

HOW DID I FEEL TODAY IN THE... (CIRCLE ONE)

Morning?
Afternoon?
Evening?

MEDICATIONS

WHAT I DID TO TAKE CARE OF MYSELF

- walk
- meditate
- bath
- cook

- workout
- yoga
- music
- tv/movie

- read
- pets
- drive
- journal

- family
- friends
- play games
- shopping

- do hobbies
- extra sleep
- favourite food
- _____

- _____
- _____
- _____
- _____

What went well? What made me feel good? What I am proud of?

1. _____
2. _____
3. _____

What contributed to negative emotions? What would I change?

1. _____
2. _____
3. _____

Daily Mood Tracker

DATE: _____   DAY: M – T – W – T – F – S – S

HOURS SLEPT

ENERGY LEVEL

STRESS LEVEL

TODAY I FELT

- loved
- valued
- proud
- grateful

- happy
- joyful
- content
- relaxed

- sick
- tired
- bored
- lazy

- angry
- anxious
- frustrated
- annoyed

- sad
- lonely
- depressed
- insecure

- productive
- motivated
- alive
- excited

- average
- normal
- fine
- OK

THREE THINGS TODAY I AM GRATEFUL FOR

1. _____
2. _____
3. _____

Water Intake (8 Glass A day):

HOW DID I FEEL TODAY IN THE... (CIRCLE ONE)

Morning?

Afternoon?

Evening?

DID I HAVE ENOUGH?   YES   NO

fruits/veggies   ☐   ☐

vitamins   ☐   ☐

fresh air   ☐   ☐

exercise   ☐   ☐

sleep   ☐   ☐

MEDICATIONS

WHAT I DID TO TAKE CARE OF MYSELF

- walk
- meditate
- bath
- cook

- workout
- yoga
- music
- tv/movie

- read
- pets
- drive
- journal

- family
- friends
- play games
- shopping

- do hobbies
- extra sleep
- favourite food
- _____

- _____
- _____
- _____
- _____

What went well? What made me feel good? What I am proud of?

1. _____
2. _____
3. _____

What contributed to negative emotions? What would I change?

1. _____
2. _____
3. _____

Daily Mood Tracker

DATE: _____

DAY: M – T – W – T – F – S – S

HOURS SLEPT	ENERGY LEVEL	STRESS LEVEL

TODAY I FELT

- loved
- valued
- proud
- grateful

- happy
- joyful
- content
- relaxed

- sick
- tired
- bored
- lazy

- angry
- anxious
- frustrated
- annoyed

- sad
- lonely
- depressed
- insecure

- productive
- motivated
- alive
- excited

- average
- normal
- fine
- OK

THREE THINGS TODAY I AM GRATEFUL FOR

1. _____
2. _____
3. _____

Water Intake (8 Glass A day):

HOW DID I FEEL TODAY IN THE... (CIRCLE ONE)

Morning?

Afternoon?

Evening?

DID I HAVE ENOUGH?

	YES	NO
fruits/veggies	☐	☐
vitamins	☐	☐
fresh air	☐	☐
exercise	☐	☐
sleep	☐	☐

MEDICATIONS

WHAT I DID TO TAKE CARE OF MYSELF

- walk
- meditate
- bath
- cook

- workout
- yoga
- music
- tv/movie

- read
- pets
- drive
- journal

- family
- friends
- play games
- shopping

- do hobbies
- extra sleep
- favourite food
- _____

- _____
- _____
- _____
- _____

What went well? What made me feel good? What I am proud of?

1. _____
2. _____
3. _____

What contributed to negative emotions? What would I change?

1. _____
2. _____
3. _____

Daily Mood Tracker

DATE: _____

DAY: M - T - W - T - F - S - S

HOURS SLEPT	ENERGY LEVEL	STRESS LEVEL

TODAY I FELT

- loved
- valued
- proud
- grateful

- happy
- joyful
- content
- relaxed

- sick
- tired
- bored
- lazy

- angry
- anxious
- frustrated
- annoyed

- sad
- lonely
- depressed
- insecure

- productive
- motivated
- alive
- excited

- average
- normal
- fine
- OK

THREE THINGS TODAY I AM GRATEFUL FOR

1. _____
2. _____
3. _____

Water Intake (8 Glass A day):

DID I HAVE ENOUGH?   YES   NO

fruits/veggies   ☐   ☐

vitamins   ☐   ☐

fresh air   ☐   ☐

exercise   ☐   ☐

sleep   ☐   ☐

HOW DID I FEEL TODAY IN THE... (CIRCLE ONE)

Morning?

Afternoon?

Evening?

MEDICATIONS

WHAT I DID TO TAKE CARE OF MYSELF

- walk
- meditate
- bath
- cook

- workout
- yoga
- music
- tv/movie

- read
- pets
- drive
- journal

- family
- friends
- play games
- shopping

- do hobbies
- extra sleep
- favourite food
- _____

- _____
- _____
- _____
- _____

What went well? What made me feel good? What I am proud of?

1. _____
2. _____
3. _____

What contributed to negative emotions? What would I change?

1. _____
2. _____
3. _____

Daily Mood Tracker

DATE: _____

DAY: M - T - W - T - F - S - S

HOURS SLEPT	ENERGY LEVEL	STRESS LEVEL

TODAY I FELT

- loved
- valued
- proud
- grateful

- happy
- joyful
- content
- relaxed

- sick
- tired
- bored
- lazy

- angry
- anxious
- frustrated
- annoyed

- sad
- lonely
- depressed
- insecure

- productive
- motivated
- alive
- excited

- average
- normal
- fine
- OK

THREE THINGS TODAY I AM GRATEFUL FOR

1. _____
2. _____
3. _____

Water Intake (8 Glass A day):

HOW DID I FEEL TODAY IN THE... (CIRCLE ONE)

Morning?

Afternoon?

Evening?

DID I HAVE ENOUGH?   YES   NO

fruits/veggies ☐ ☐

vitamins ☐ ☐

fresh air ☐ ☐

exercise ☐ ☐

sleep ☐ ☐

MEDICATIONS

WHAT I DID TO TAKE CARE OF MYSELF

- walk
- meditate
- bath
- cook

- workout
- yoga
- music
- tv/movie

- read
- pets
- drive
- journal

- family
- friends
- play games
- shopping

- do hobbies
- extra sleep
- favourite food
- _____

- _____
- _____
- _____
- _____

What went well? What made me feel good? What I am proud of?

1. _____
2. _____
3. _____

What contributed to negative emotions? What would I change?

1. _____
2. _____
3. _____

Daily Mood Tracker

DATE: _____   DAY: M – T – W – T – F – S – S

HOURS SLEPT	ENERGY LEVEL	STRESS LEVEL

TODAY I FELT

- loved
- valued
- proud
- grateful

- happy
- joyful
- content
- relaxed

- sick
- tired
- bored
- lazy

- angry
- anxious
- frustrated
- annoyed

- sad
- lonely
- depressed
- insecure

- productive
- motivated
- alive
- excited

- average
- normal
- fine
- OK

THREE THINGS TODAY I AM GRATEFUL FOR

1. _____
2. _____
3. _____

Water Intake (8 Glass A day):

DID I HAVE ENOUGH?	YES	NO
fruits/veggies	☐	☐
vitamins	☐	☐
fresh air	☐	☐
exercise	☐	☐
sleep	☐	☐

HOW DID I FEEL TODAY IN THE... (CIRCLE ONE)

Morning?

Afternoon?

Evening?

MEDICATIONS

WHAT I DID TO TAKE CARE OF MYSELF

- walk
- meditate
- bath
- cook

- workout
- yoga
- music
- tv/movie

- read
- pets
- drive
- journal

- family
- friends
- play games
- shopping

- do hobbies
- extra sleep
- favourite food
- _____

- _____
- _____
- _____
- _____

What went well? What made me feel good? What I am proud of?

1. _____
2. _____
3. _____

What contributed to negative emotions? What would I change?

1. _____
2. _____
3. _____

Daily Mood Tracker

DATE: _____

DAY: M – T – W – T – F – S – S

HOURS SLEPT

ENERGY LEVEL

STRESS LEVEL

TODAY I FELT

- loved
- valued
- proud
- grateful

- happy
- joyful
- content
- relaxed

- sick
- tired
- bored
- lazy

- angry
- anxious
- frustrated
- annoyed

- sad
- lonely
- depressed
- insecure

- productive
- motivated
- alive
- excited

- average
- normal
- fine
- OK

THREE THINGS TODAY I AM GRATEFUL FOR

1. _____
2. _____
3. _____

Water Intake (8 Glass A day):

DID I HAVE ENOUGH?   YES   NO

fruits/veggies   ☐   ☐

vitamins   ☐   ☐

fresh air   ☐   ☐

exercise   ☐   ☐

sleep   ☐   ☐

HOW DID I FEEL TODAY IN THE... (CIRCLE ONE)

Morning?

Afternoon?

Evening?

MEDICATIONS

WHAT I DID TO TAKE CARE OF MYSELF

- walk
- meditate
- bath
- cook

- workout
- yoga
- music
- tv/movie

- read
- pets
- drive
- journal

- family
- friends
- play games
- shopping

- do hobbies
- extra sleep
- favourite food
- _____

- _____
- _____
- _____
- _____

What went well? What made me feel good? What I am proud of?

1. _____
2. _____
3. _____

What contributed to negative emotions? What would I change?

1. _____
2. _____
3. _____

Daily Mood Tracker

DATE: _____   DAY: M – T – W – T – F – S – S

HOURS SLEPT	ENERGY LEVEL	STRESS LEVEL

TODAY I FELT

- loved
- valued
- proud
- grateful

- happy
- joyful
- content
- relaxed

- sick
- tired
- bored
- lazy

- angry
- anxious
- frustrated
- annoyed

- sad
- lonely
- depressed
- insecure

- productive
- motivated
- alive
- excited

- average
- normal
- fine
- OK

THREE THINGS TODAY I AM GRATEFUL FOR

1. _____
2. _____
3. _____

Water Intake (8 Glass A day):

HOW DID I FEEL TODAY IN THE... (CIRCLE ONE)

Morning?

Afternoon?

Evening?

DID I HAVE ENOUGH?   YES   NO

fruits/veggies   ☐   ☐

vitamins   ☐   ☐

fresh air   ☐   ☐

exercise   ☐   ☐

sleep   ☐   ☐

MEDICATIONS

WHAT I DID TO TAKE CARE OF MYSELF

- walk
- meditate
- bath
- cook

- workout
- yoga
- music
- tv/movie

- read
- pets
- drive
- journal

- family
- friends
- play games
- shopping

- do hobbies
- extra sleep
- favourite food
- _____

- _____
- _____
- _____
- _____

What went well? What made me feel good? What I am proud of?

1. _____
2. _____
3. _____

What contributed to negative emotions? What would I change?

1. _____
2. _____
3. _____

Daily Mood Tracker

DATE: _____

DAY: M – T – W – T – F – S – S

HOURS SLEPT	ENERGY LEVEL	STRESS LEVEL

TODAY I FELT

- loved
- valued
- proud
- grateful

- happy
- joyful
- content
- relaxed

- sick
- tired
- bored
- lazy

- angry
- anxious
- frustrated
- annoyed

- sad
- lonely
- depressed
- insecure

- productive
- motivated
- alive
- excited

- average
- normal
- fine
- OK

THREE THINGS TODAY I AM GRATEFUL FOR

1. _____
2. _____
3. _____

Water Intake (8 Glass A day):

DID I HAVE ENOUGH? YES NO

- fruits/veggies ☐ ☐
- vitamins ☐ ☐
- fresh air ☐ ☐
- exercise ☐ ☐
- sleep ☐ ☐

HOW DID I FEEL TODAY IN THE... (CIRCLE ONE)

Morning?

Afternoon?

Evening?

MEDICATIONS

WHAT I DID TO TAKE CARE OF MYSELF

- walk
- meditate
- bath
- cook

- workout
- yoga
- music
- tv/movie

- read
- pets
- drive
- journal

- family
- friends
- play games
- shopping

- do hobbies
- extra sleep
- favourite food
- _____

- _____
- _____
- _____
- _____

What went well? What made me feel good? What I am proud of?

1. _____
2. _____
3. _____

What contributed to negative emotions? What would I change?

1. _____
2. _____
3. _____

Daily Mood Tracker

DATE: _____

DAY: M – T – W – T – F – S – S

HOURS SLEPT	ENERGY LEVEL	STRESS LEVEL

TODAY I FELT

• loved	• happy	• sick	• angry	• sad	• productive	• average
• valued	• joyful	• tired	• anxious	• lonely	• motivated	• normal
• proud	• content	• bored	• frustrated	• depressed	• alive	• fine
• grateful	• relaxed	• lazy	• annoyed	• insecure	• excited	• OK

THREE THINGS TODAY I AM GRATEFUL FOR

1. _____
2. _____
3. _____

Water Intake (8 Glass A day):

DID I HAVE ENOUGH?   YES   NO

fruits/veggies   ☐   ☐

vitamins   ☐   ☐

fresh air   ☐   ☐

exercise   ☐   ☐

sleep   ☐   ☐

HOW DID I FEEL TODAY IN THE... (CIRCLE ONE)

Morning?

Afternoon?

Evening?

MEDICATIONS

WHAT I DID TO TAKE CARE OF MYSELF

• walk	• workout	• read	• family	• do hobbies	• _____
• meditate	• yoga	• pets	• friends	• extra sleep	• _____
• bath	• music	• drive	• play games	• favourite food	• _____
• cook	• tv/movie	• journal	• shopping	• _____	• _____

What went well? What made me feel good? What I am proud of?

1. _____
2. _____
3. _____

What contributed to negative emotions? What would I change?

1. _____
2. _____
3. _____

Daily Mood Tracker

DATE: _____

DAY: M - T - W - T - F - S - S

HOURS SLEPT

ENERGY LEVEL

STRESS LEVEL

TODAY I FELT

- loved
- valued
- proud
- grateful

- happy
- joyful
- content
- relaxed

- sick
- tired
- bored
- lazy

- angry
- anxious
- frustrated
- annoyed

- sad
- lonely
- depressed
- insecure

- productive
- motivated
- alive
- excited

- average
- normal
- fine
- OK

THREE THINGS TODAY I AM GRATEFUL FOR

1. _____
2. _____
3. _____

Water Intake (8 Glass A day):

DID I HAVE ENOUGH?   YES   NO

fruits/veggies   ☐   ☐

vitamins   ☐   ☐

fresh air   ☐   ☐

exercise   ☐   ☐

sleep   ☐   ☐

HOW DID I FEEL TODAY IN THE... (CIRCLE ONE)

Morning?

Afternoon?

Evening?

MEDICATIONS

WHAT I DID TO TAKE CARE OF MYSELF

- walk
- meditate
- bath
- cook

- workout
- yoga
- music
- tv/movie

- read
- pets
- drive
- journal

- family
- friends
- play games
- shopping

- do hobbies
- extra sleep
- favourite food
- _____

- _____
- _____
- _____
- _____

What went well? What made me feel good? What I am proud of?

1. _____
2. _____
3. _____

What contributed to negative emotions? What would I change?

1. _____
2. _____
3. _____

Daily Mood Tracker

DATE: _____

DAY: M - T - W - T - F - S - S

HOURS SLEPT	ENERGY LEVEL	STRESS LEVEL

TODAY I FELT

- loved
- valued
- proud
- grateful

- happy
- joyful
- content
- relaxed

- sick
- tired
- bored
- lazy

- angry
- anxious
- frustrated
- annoyed

- sad
- lonely
- depressed
- insecure

- productive
- motivated
- alive
- excited

- average
- normal
- fine
- OK

THREE THINGS TODAY I AM GRATEFUL FOR

1. _____
2. _____
3. _____

Water Intake (8 Glass A day):

DID I HAVE ENOUGH?   YES   NO

fruits/veggies   ☐   ☐

vitamins   ☐   ☐

fresh air   ☐   ☐

exercise   ☐   ☐

sleep   ☐   ☐

HOW DID I FEEL TODAY IN THE... (CIRCLE ONE)

Morning?

Afternoon?

Evening?

MEDICATIONS

WHAT I DID TO TAKE CARE OF MYSELF

- walk
- meditate
- bath
- cook

- workout
- yoga
- music
- tv/movie

- read
- pets
- drive
- journal

- family
- friends
- play games
- shopping

- do hobbies
- extra sleep
- favourite food
- _____

- _____
- _____
- _____
- _____

What went well? What made me feel good? What I am proud of?

1. _____
2. _____
3. _____

What contributed to negative emotions? What would I change?

1. _____
2. _____
3. _____

Daily Mood Tracker

DATE: _____   DAY: M - T - W - T - F - S - S

HOURS SLEPT	ENERGY LEVEL	STRESS LEVEL

TODAY I FELT

- loved
- valued
- proud
- grateful

- happy
- joyful
- content
- relaxed

- sick
- tired
- bored
- lazy

- angry
- anxious
- frustrated
- annoyed

- sad
- lonely
- depressed
- insecure

- productive
- motivated
- alive
- excited

- average
- normal
- fine
- OK

THREE THINGS TODAY I AM GRATEFUL FOR

1. _____
2. _____
3. _____

Water Intake (8 Glass A day):

HOW DID I FEEL TODAY IN THE... (CIRCLE ONE)

Morning?

Afternoon?

Evening?

DID I HAVE ENOUGH?   YES   NO

fruits/veggies   ☐   ☐

vitamins   ☐   ☐

fresh air   ☐   ☐

exercise   ☐   ☐

sleep   ☐   ☐

MEDICATIONS

WHAT I DID TO TAKE CARE OF MYSELF

- walk
- meditate
- bath
- cook

- workout
- yoga
- music
- tv/movie

- read
- pets
- drive
- journal

- family
- friends
- play games
- shopping

- do hobbies
- extra sleep
- favourite food
- _____

- _____
- _____
- _____
- _____

What went well? What made me feel good? What I am proud of?

1. _____
2. _____
3. _____

What contributed to negative emotions? What would I change?

1. _____
2. _____
3. _____

Daily Mood Tracker

DATE: _____

DAY: M - T - W - T - F - S - S

HOURS SLEPT

ENERGY LEVEL

STRESS LEVEL

TODAY I FELT

- loved
- valued
- proud
- grateful

- happy
- joyful
- content
- relaxed

- sick
- tired
- bored
- lazy

- angry
- anxious
- frustrated
- annoyed

- sad
- lonely
- depressed
- insecure

- productive
- motivated
- alive
- excited

- average
- normal
- fine
- OK

THREE THINGS TODAY I AM GRATEFUL FOR

1. _____
2. _____
3. _____

Water Intake (8 Glass A day):

HOW DID I FEEL TODAY IN THE... (CIRCLE ONE)

Morning?

Afternoon?

Evening?

DID I HAVE ENOUGH?

	YES	NO
fruits/veggies	☐	☐
vitamins	☐	☐
fresh air	☐	☐
exercise	☐	☐
sleep	☐	☐

MEDICATIONS

WHAT I DID TO TAKE CARE OF MYSELF

- walk
- meditate
- bath
- cook

- workout
- yoga
- music
- tv/movie

- read
- pets
- drive
- journal

- family
- friends
- play games
- shopping

- do hobbies
- extra sleep
- favourite food
- _____

- _____
- _____
- _____
- _____

What went well? What made me feel good? What I am proud of?

1. _____
2. _____
3. _____

What contributed to negative emotions? What would I change?

1. _____
2. _____
3. _____

Daily Mood Tracker

DATE: _____

DAY: M - T - W - T - F - S - S

HOURS SLEPT	ENERGY LEVEL	STRESS LEVEL

TODAY I FELT

- loved
- valued
- proud
- grateful

- happy
- joyful
- content
- relaxed

- sick
- tired
- bored
- lazy

- angry
- anxious
- frustrated
- annoyed

- sad
- lonely
- depressed
- insecure

- productive
- motivated
- alive
- excited

- average
- normal
- fine
- OK

THREE THINGS TODAY I AM GRATEFUL FOR

1. _____
2. _____
3. _____

Water Intake (8 Glass A day):

DID I HAVE ENOUGH?   YES   NO

fruits/veggies ☐ ☐

vitamins ☐ ☐

fresh air ☐ ☐

exercise ☐ ☐

sleep ☐ ☐

HOW DID I FEEL TODAY IN THE... (CIRCLE ONE)

Morning?

Afternoon?

Evening?

MEDICATIONS

WHAT I DID TO TAKE CARE OF MYSELF

- walk
- meditate
- bath
- cook

- workout
- yoga
- music
- tv/movie

- read
- pets
- drive
- journal

- family
- friends
- play games
- shopping

- do hobbies
- extra sleep
- favourite food
- _____

- _____
- _____
- _____
- _____

What went well? What made me feel good? What I am proud of?

1. _____
2. _____
3. _____

What contributed to negative emotions? What would I change?

1. _____
2. _____
3. _____

Daily Mood Tracker

DATE: _____

DAY: M – T – W – T – F – S – S

HOURS SLEPT

ENERGY LEVEL

STRESS LEVEL

TODAY I FELT

- loved
- valued
- proud
- grateful

- happy
- joyful
- content
- relaxed

- sick
- tired
- bored
- lazy

- angry
- anxious
- frustrated
- annoyed

- sad
- lonely
- depressed
- insecure

- productive
- motivated
- alive
- excited

- average
- normal
- fine
- OK

THREE THINGS TODAY I AM GRATEFUL FOR

1. _____
2. _____
3. _____

Water Intake (8 Glass A day):

DID I HAVE ENOUGH?   YES   NO

fruits/veggies   ☐ ☐

vitamins   ☐ ☐

fresh air   ☐ ☐

exercise   ☐ ☐

sleep   ☐ ☐

HOW DID I FEEL TODAY IN THE... (CIRCLE ONE)

Morning?

Afternoon?

Evening?

MEDICATIONS

WHAT I DID TO TAKE CARE OF MYSELF

- walk
- meditate
- bath
- cook

- workout
- yoga
- music
- tv/movie

- read
- pets
- drive
- journal

- family
- friends
- play games
- shopping

- do hobbies
- extra sleep
- favourite food
- _____

- _____
- _____
- _____
- _____

What went well? What made me feel good? What I am proud of?

1. _____
2. _____
3. _____

What contributed to negative emotions? What would I change?

1. _____
2. _____
3. _____

Daily Mood Tracker

DATE: _____   DAY: M – T – W – T – F – S – S

HOURS SLEPT	ENERGY LEVEL	STRESS LEVEL

TODAY I FELT

- loved
- valued
- proud
- grateful

- happy
- joyful
- content
- relaxed

- sick
- tired
- bored
- lazy

- angry
- anxious
- frustrated
- annoyed

- sad
- lonely
- depressed
- insecure

- productive
- motivated
- alive
- excited

- average
- normal
- fine
- OK

THREE THINGS TODAY I AM GRATEFUL FOR

1. _____
2. _____
3. _____

Water Intake (8 Glass A day):

DID I HAVE ENOUGH?   YES   NO

fruits/veggies   ☐   ☐

vitamins   ☐   ☐

fresh air   ☐   ☐

exercise   ☐   ☐

sleep   ☐   ☐

HOW DID I FEEL TODAY IN THE... (CIRCLE ONE)

Morning?

Afternoon?

Evening?

MEDICATIONS

WHAT I DID TO TAKE CARE OF MYSELF

- walk
- meditate
- bath
- cook

- workout
- yoga
- music
- tv/movie

- read
- pets
- drive
- journal

- family
- friends
- play games
- shopping

- do hobbies
- extra sleep
- favourite food
- _____

- _____
- _____
- _____
- _____

What went well? What made me feel good? What I am proud of?

1. _____
2. _____
3. _____

What contributed to negative emotions? What would I change?

1. _____
2. _____
3. _____

Daily Mood Tracker

DATE: _____

DAY: M - T - W - T - F - S - S

HOURS SLEPT

ENERGY LEVEL

STRESS LEVEL

TODAY I FELT

- loved
- valued
- proud
- grateful

- happy
- joyful
- content
- relaxed

- sick
- tired
- bored
- lazy

- angry
- anxious
- frustrated
- annoyed

- sad
- lonely
- depressed
- insecure

- productive
- motivated
- alive
- excited

- average
- normal
- fine
- OK

THREE THINGS TODAY I AM GRATEFUL FOR

1. _____
2. _____
3. _____

Water Intake (8 Glass A day):

HOW DID I FEEL TODAY IN THE... (CIRCLE ONE)

Morning?

Afternoon?

Evening?

DID I HAVE ENOUGH?

	YES	NO
fruits/veggies	☐	☐
vitamins	☐	☐
fresh air	☐	☐
exercise	☐	☐
sleep	☐	☐

MEDICATIONS

WHAT I DID TO TAKE CARE OF MYSELF

- walk
- meditate
- bath
- cook

- workout
- yoga
- music
- tv/movie

- read
- pets
- drive
- journal

- family
- friends
- play games
- shopping

- do hobbies
- extra sleep
- favourite food
- _____

- _____
- _____
- _____
- _____

What went well? What made me feel good? What I am proud of?

1. _____
2. _____
3. _____

What contributed to negative emotions? What would I change?

1. _____
2. _____
3. _____

Daily Mood Tracker

DATE: _____

DAY: M - T - W - T - F - S - S

HOURS SLEPT

ENERGY LEVEL

STRESS LEVEL

TODAY I FELT

- loved
- valued
- proud
- grateful

- happy
- joyful
- content
- relaxed

- sick
- tired
- bored
- lazy

- angry
- anxious
- frustrated
- annoyed

- sad
- lonely
- depressed
- insecure

- productive
- motivated
- alive
- excited

- average
- normal
- fine
- OK

THREE THINGS TODAY I AM GRATEFUL FOR

1. _____
2. _____
3. _____

Water Intake (8 Glass A day):

DID I HAVE ENOUGH?   YES   NO

fruits/veggies   ☐   ☐

vitamins   ☐   ☐

fresh air   ☐   ☐

exercise   ☐   ☐

sleep   ☐   ☐

HOW DID I FEEL TODAY IN THE... (CIRCLE ONE)

Morning?

Afternoon?

Evening?

MEDICATIONS

WHAT I DID TO TAKE CARE OF MYSELF

- walk
- meditate
- bath
- cook

- workout
- yoga
- music
- tv/movie

- read
- pets
- drive
- journal

- family
- friends
- play games
- shopping

- do hobbies
- extra sleep
- favourite food
- _____

- _____
- _____
- _____
- _____

What went well? What made me feel good? What I am proud of?

1. _____
2. _____
3. _____

What contributed to negative emotions? What would I change?

1. _____
2. _____
3. _____

Daily Mood Tracker

DATE: _____   DAY: M – T – W – T – F – S – S

HOURS SLEPT	ENERGY LEVEL	STRESS LEVEL

TODAY I FELT

- loved
- valued
- proud
- grateful

- happy
- joyful
- content
- relaxed

- sick
- tired
- bored
- lazy

- angry
- anxious
- frustrated
- annoyed

- sad
- lonely
- depressed
- insecure

- productive
- motivated
- alive
- excited

- average
- normal
- fine
- OK

THREE THINGS TODAY I AM GRATEFUL FOR

1. _____
2. _____
3. _____

Water Intake (8 Glass A day):

HOW DID I FEEL TODAY IN THE... (CIRCLE ONE)

Morning?

Afternoon?

Evening?

DID I HAVE ENOUGH?   YES   NO

fruits/veggies   ☐   ☐

vitamins   ☐   ☐

fresh air   ☐   ☐

exercise   ☐   ☐

sleep   ☐   ☐

MEDICATIONS

WHAT I DID TO TAKE CARE OF MYSELF

- walk
- meditate
- bath
- cook

- workout
- yoga
- music
- tv/movie

- read
- pets
- drive
- journal

- family
- friends
- play games
- shopping

- do hobbies
- extra sleep
- favourite food
- _____

- _____
- _____
- _____
- _____

What went well? What made me feel good? What I am proud of?

1. _____
2. _____
3. _____

What contributed to negative emotions? What would I change?

1. _____
2. _____
3. _____

Daily Mood Tracker

DATE: _____

DAY: M – T – W – T – F – S – S

HOURS SLEPT	ENERGY LEVEL	STRESS LEVEL

TODAY I FELT

- loved
- valued
- proud
- grateful

- happy
- joyful
- content
- relaxed

- sick
- tired
- bored
- lazy

- angry
- anxious
- frustrated
- annoyed

- sad
- lonely
- depressed
- insecure

- productive
- motivated
- alive
- excited

- average
- normal
- fine
- OK

THREE THINGS TODAY I AM GRATEFUL FOR

1. _____
2. _____
3. _____

Water Intake (8 Glass A day):

DID I HAVE ENOUGH?   YES   NO

	YES	NO
fruits/veggies	☐	☐
vitamins	☐	☐
fresh air	☐	☐
exercise	☐	☐
sleep	☐	☐

HOW DID I FEEL TODAY IN THE... (CIRCLE ONE)

Morning?
Afternoon?
Evening?

MEDICATIONS

WHAT I DID TO TAKE CARE OF MYSELF

- walk
- meditate
- bath
- cook

- workout
- yoga
- music
- tv/movie

- read
- pets
- drive
- journal

- family
- friends
- play games
- shopping

- do hobbies
- extra sleep
- favourite food
- _____

- _____
- _____
- _____
- _____

What went well? What made me feel good? What I am proud of?

1. _____
2. _____
3. _____

What contributed to negative emotions? What would I change?

1. _____
2. _____
3. _____

Daily Mood Tracker

DATE: _____   DAY: M – T – W – T – F – S – S

HOURS SLEPT	ENERGY LEVEL	STRESS LEVEL

TODAY I FELT

- loved
- valued
- proud
- grateful

- happy
- joyful
- content
- relaxed

- sick
- tired
- bored
- lazy

- angry
- anxious
- frustrated
- annoyed

- sad
- lonely
- depressed
- insecure

- productive
- motivated
- alive
- excited

- average
- normal
- fine
- OK

THREE THINGS TODAY I AM GRATEFUL FOR

1. _____
2. _____
3. _____

Water Intake (8 Glass A day):

DID I HAVE ENOUGH?   YES   NO

fruits/veggies   ☐   ☐

vitamins   ☐   ☐

fresh air   ☐   ☐

exercise   ☐   ☐

sleep   ☐   ☐

HOW DID I FEEL TODAY IN THE... (CIRCLE ONE)

Morning?

Afternoon?

Evening?

MEDICATIONS

WHAT I DID TO TAKE CARE OF MYSELF

- walk
- meditate
- bath
- cook

- workout
- yoga
- music
- tv/movie

- read
- pets
- drive
- journal

- family
- friends
- play games
- shopping

- do hobbies
- extra sleep
- favourite food
- _____

- _____
- _____
- _____
- _____

What went well? What made me feel good? What I am proud of?

1. _____
2. _____
3. _____

What contributed to negative emotions? What would I change?

1. _____
2. _____
3. _____

Daily Mood Tracker

DATE: _____

DAY: M - T - W - T - F - S - S

HOURS SLEPT	ENERGY LEVEL	STRESS LEVEL

TODAY I FELT

- loved
- valued
- proud
- grateful

- happy
- joyful
- content
- relaxed

- sick
- tired
- bored
- lazy

- angry
- anxious
- frustrated
- annoyed

- sad
- lonely
- depressed
- insecure

- productive
- motivated
- alive
- excited

- average
- normal
- fine
- OK

THREE THINGS TODAY I AM GRATEFUL FOR

1. _____
2. _____
3. _____

Water Intake (8 Glass A day):

HOW DID I FEEL TODAY IN THE... (CIRCLE ONE)

Morning?

Afternoon?

Evening?

DID I HAVE ENOUGH? YES NO

fruits/veggies ☐ ☐

vitamins ☐ ☐

fresh air ☐ ☐

exercise ☐ ☐

sleep ☐ ☐

MEDICATIONS

WHAT I DID TO TAKE CARE OF MYSELF

- walk
- meditate
- bath
- cook

- workout
- yoga
- music
- tv/movie

- read
- pets
- drive
- journal

- family
- friends
- play games
- shopping

- do hobbies
- extra sleep
- favourite food
- _____

- _____
- _____
- _____
- _____

What went well? What made me feel good? What I am proud of?

1. _____
2. _____
3. _____

What contributed to negative emotions? What would I change?

1. _____
2. _____
3. _____

Daily Mood Tracker

DATE: _____   DAY: M - T - W - T - F - S - S

HOURS SLEPT	ENERGY LEVEL	STRESS LEVEL

TODAY I FELT

- loved
- valued
- proud
- grateful

- happy
- joyful
- content
- relaxed

- sick
- tired
- bored
- lazy

- angry
- anxious
- frustrated
- annoyed

- sad
- lonely
- depressed
- insecure

- productive
- motivated
- alive
- excited

- average
- normal
- fine
- OK

THREE THINGS TODAY I AM GRATEFUL FOR

1. _____
2. _____
3. _____

Water Intake (8 Glass A day):

DID I HAVE ENOUGH?   YES   NO

fruits/veggies   ☐   ☐

vitamins   ☐   ☐

fresh air   ☐   ☐

exercise   ☐   ☐

sleep   ☐   ☐

HOW DID I FEEL TODAY IN THE... (CIRCLE ONE)

Morning?

Afternoon?

Evening?

MEDICATIONS

WHAT I DID TO TAKE CARE OF MYSELF

- walk
- meditate
- bath
- cook

- workout
- yoga
- music
- tv/movie

- read
- pets
- drive
- journal

- family
- friends
- play games
- shopping

- do hobbies
- extra sleep
- favourite food
- _____

- _____
- _____
- _____
- _____

What went well? What made me feel good? What I am proud of?

1. _____
2. _____
3. _____

What contributed to negative emotions? What would I change?

1. _____
2. _____
3. _____

Daily Mood Tracker

DATE: _____

DAY: M – T – W – T – F – S – S

HOURS SLEPT	ENERGY LEVEL	STRESS LEVEL

TODAY I FELT

- loved
- valued
- proud
- grateful

- happy
- joyful
- content
- relaxed

- sick
- tired
- bored
- lazy

- angry
- anxious
- frustrated
- annoyed

- sad
- lonely
- depressed
- insecure

- productive
- motivated
- alive
- excited

- average
- normal
- fine
- OK

THREE THINGS TODAY I AM GRATEFUL FOR

1. _____
2. _____
3. _____

Water Intake (8 Glass A day):

DID I HAVE ENOUGH?   YES   NO

fruits/veggies   ☐   ☐

vitamins   ☐   ☐

fresh air   ☐   ☐

exercise   ☐   ☐

sleep   ☐   ☐

HOW DID I FEEL TODAY IN THE... (CIRCLE ONE)

Morning?

Afternoon?

Evening?

MEDICATIONS

WHAT I DID TO TAKE CARE OF MYSELF

- walk
- meditate
- bath
- cook

- workout
- yoga
- music
- tv/movie

- read
- pets
- drive
- journal

- family
- friends
- play games
- shopping

- do hobbies
- extra sleep
- favourite food
- _____

- _____
- _____
- _____
- _____

What went well? What made me feel good? What I am proud of?

1. _____
2. _____
3. _____

What contributed to negative emotions? What would I change?

1. _____
2. _____
3. _____

Daily Mood Tracker

DATE: _____

DAY: M – T – W – T – F – S – S

HOURS SLEPT

ENERGY LEVEL

STRESS LEVEL

TODAY I FELT

- loved
- valued
- proud
- grateful

- happy
- joyful
- content
- relaxed

- sick
- tired
- bored
- lazy

- angry
- anxious
- frustrated
- annoyed

- sad
- lonely
- depressed
- insecure

- productive
- motivated
- alive
- excited

- average
- normal
- fine
- OK

THREE THINGS TODAY I AM GRATEFUL FOR

1. _____
2. _____
3. _____

Water Intake (8 Glass A day):

DID I HAVE ENOUGH?   YES   NO

fruits/veggies   ☐   ☐

vitamins   ☐   ☐

fresh air   ☐   ☐

exercise   ☐   ☐

sleep   ☐   ☐

HOW DID I FEEL TODAY IN THE... (CIRCLE ONE)

Morning?

Afternoon?

Evening?

MEDICATIONS

WHAT I DID TO TAKE CARE OF MYSELF

- walk
- meditate
- bath
- cook

- workout
- yoga
- music
- tv/movie

- read
- pets
- drive
- journal

- family
- friends
- play games
- shopping

- do hobbies
- extra sleep
- favourite food
- _____

- _____
- _____
- _____
- _____

What went well? What made me feel good? What I am proud of?

1. _____
2. _____
3. _____

What contributed to negative emotions? What would I change?

1. _____
2. _____
3. _____

Daily Mood Tracker

DATE: _____

DAY: M – T – W – T – F – S – S

HOURS SLEPT	ENERGY LEVEL	STRESS LEVEL

TODAY I FELT

- loved
- valued
- proud
- grateful

- happy
- joyful
- content
- relaxed

- sick
- tired
- bored
- lazy

- angry
- anxious
- frustrated
- annoyed

- sad
- lonely
- depressed
- insecure

- productive
- motivated
- alive
- excited

- average
- normal
- fine
- OK

THREE THINGS TODAY I AM GRATEFUL FOR

1. _____
2. _____
3. _____

Water Intake (8 Glass A day):

DID I HAVE ENOUGH?

	YES	NO
fruits/veggies	☐	☐
vitamins	☐	☐
fresh air	☐	☐
exercise	☐	☐
sleep	☐	☐

HOW DID I FEEL TODAY IN THE... (CIRCLE ONE)

Morning?

Afternoon?

Evening?

MEDICATIONS

WHAT I DID TO TAKE CARE OF MYSELF

- walk
- meditate
- bath
- cook

- workout
- yoga
- music
- tv/movie

- read
- pets
- drive
- journal

- family
- friends
- play games
- shopping

- do hobbies
- extra sleep
- favourite food
- _____

- _____
- _____
- _____
- _____

What went well? What made me feel good? What I am proud of?

1. _____
2. _____
3. _____

What contributed to negative emotions? What would I change?

1. _____
2. _____
3. _____

Daily Mood Tracker

DATE: _____   DAY: M – T – W – T – F – S – S

HOURS SLEPT	ENERGY LEVEL	STRESS LEVEL

TODAY I FELT

- loved
- valued
- proud
- grateful

- happy
- joyful
- content
- relaxed

- sick
- tired
- bored
- lazy

- angry
- anxious
- frustrated
- annoyed

- sad
- lonely
- depressed
- insecure

- productive
- motivated
- alive
- excited

- average
- normal
- fine
- OK

THREE THINGS TODAY I AM GRATEFUL FOR

1. _____
2. _____
3. _____

Water Intake (8 Glass A day):

DID I HAVE ENOUGH?   YES   NO

fruits/veggies   ☐   ☐

vitamins   ☐   ☐

fresh air   ☐   ☐

exercise   ☐   ☐

sleep   ☐   ☐

HOW DID I FEEL TODAY IN THE... (CIRCLE ONE)

Morning?

Afternoon?

Evening?

MEDICATIONS

WHAT I DID TO TAKE CARE OF MYSELF

- walk
- meditate
- bath
- cook

- workout
- yoga
- music
- tv/movie

- read
- pets
- drive
- journal

- family
- friends
- play games
- shopping

- do hobbies
- extra sleep
- favourite food
- _____

- _____
- _____
- _____
- _____

What went well? What made me feel good? What I am proud of?

1. _____
2. _____
3. _____

What contributed to negative emotions? What would I change?

1. _____
2. _____
3. _____

Daily Mood Tracker

DATE: _____

DAY: M – T – W – T – F – S – S

HOURS SLEPT

ENERGY LEVEL

STRESS LEVEL

TODAY I FELT

- loved
- valued
- proud
- grateful

- happy
- joyful
- content
- relaxed

- sick
- tired
- bored
- lazy

- angry
- anxious
- frustrated
- annoyed

- sad
- lonely
- depressed
- insecure

- productive
- motivated
- alive
- excited

- average
- normal
- fine
- OK

THREE THINGS TODAY I AM GRATEFUL FOR

1. _____
2. _____
3. _____

Water Intake (8 Glass A day):

DID I HAVE ENOUGH?

	YES	NO
fruits/veggies	☐	☐
vitamins	☐	☐
fresh air	☐	☐
exercise	☐	☐
sleep	☐	☐

HOW DID I FEEL TODAY IN THE... (CIRCLE ONE)

Morning?

Afternoon?

Evening?

MEDICATIONS

WHAT I DID TO TAKE CARE OF MYSELF

- walk
- meditate
- bath
- cook

- workout
- yoga
- music
- tv/movie

- read
- pets
- drive
- journal

- family
- friends
- play games
- shopping

- do hobbies
- extra sleep
- favourite food
- _____

- _____
- _____
- _____
- _____

What went well? What made me feel good? What I am proud of?

1. _____
2. _____
3. _____

What contributed to negative emotions? What would I change?

1. _____
2. _____
3. _____

Daily Mood Tracker

DATE: _____

DAY: M – T – W – T – F – S – S

HOURS SLEPT

ENERGY LEVEL

STRESS LEVEL

TODAY I FELT

- loved
- valued
- proud
- grateful

- happy
- joyful
- content
- relaxed

- sick
- tired
- bored
- lazy

- angry
- anxious
- frustrated
- annoyed

- sad
- lonely
- depressed
- insecure

- productive
- motivated
- alive
- excited

- average
- normal
- fine
- OK

THREE THINGS TODAY I AM GRATEFUL FOR

1. _____
2. _____
3. _____

Water Intake (8 Glass A day):

DID I HAVE ENOUGH?   YES   NO

fruits/veggies   ☐   ☐

vitamins   ☐   ☐

fresh air   ☐   ☐

exercise   ☐   ☐

sleep   ☐   ☐

HOW DID I FEEL TODAY IN THE... (CIRCLE ONE)

Morning?

Afternoon?

Evening?

MEDICATIONS

WHAT I DID TO TAKE CARE OF MYSELF

- walk
- meditate
- bath
- cook

- workout
- yoga
- music
- tv/movie

- read
- pets
- drive
- journal

- family
- friends
- play games
- shopping

- do hobbies
- extra sleep
- favourite food
- _____

- _____
- _____
- _____
- _____

What went well? What made me feel good? What I am proud of?

1. _____
2. _____
3. _____

What contributed to negative emotions? What would I change?

1. _____
2. _____
3. _____

Daily Mood Tracker

DATE: _____

DAY: M – T – W – T – F – S – S

HOURS SLEPT

ENERGY LEVEL

STRESS LEVEL

TODAY I FELT

- loved
- valued
- proud
- grateful

- happy
- joyful
- content
- relaxed

- sick
- tired
- bored
- lazy

- angry
- anxious
- frustrated
- annoyed

- sad
- lonely
- depressed
- insecure

- productive
- motivated
- alive
- excited

- average
- normal
- fine
- OK

THREE THINGS TODAY I AM GRATEFUL FOR

1. _____
2. _____
3. _____

Water Intake (8 Glass A day):

DID I HAVE ENOUGH?   YES   NO

fruits/veggies   ☐   ☐

vitamins   ☐   ☐

fresh air   ☐   ☐

exercise   ☐   ☐

sleep   ☐   ☐

HOW DID I FEEL TODAY IN THE... (CIRCLE ONE)

Morning?

Afternoon?

Evening?

MEDICATIONS

WHAT I DID TO TAKE CARE OF MYSELF

- walk
- meditate
- bath
- cook

- workout
- yoga
- music
- tv/movie

- read
- pets
- drive
- journal

- family
- friends
- play games
- shopping

- do hobbies
- extra sleep
- favourite food
- _____

- _____
- _____
- _____
- _____

What went well? What made me feel good? What I am proud of?

1. _____
2. _____
3. _____

What contributed to negative emotions? What would I change?

1. _____
2. _____
3. _____

Daily Mood Tracker

DATE: _____

DAY: M – T – W – T – F – S – S

HOURS SLEPT

ENERGY LEVEL

STRESS LEVEL

TODAY I FELT

- loved
- valued
- proud
- grateful

- happy
- joyful
- content
- relaxed

- sick
- tired
- bored
- lazy

- angry
- anxious
- frustrated
- annoyed

- sad
- lonely
- depressed
- insecure

- productive
- motivated
- alive
- excited

- average
- normal
- fine
- OK

THREE THINGS TODAY I AM GRATEFUL FOR

1. _____
2. _____
3. _____

Water Intake (8 Glass A day):

DID I HAVE ENOUGH?   YES   NO

fruits/veggies   ☐   ☐

vitamins   ☐   ☐

fresh air   ☐   ☐

exercise   ☐   ☐

sleep   ☐   ☐

HOW DID I FEEL TODAY IN THE... (CIRCLE ONE)

Morning?

Afternoon?

Evening?

MEDICATIONS

WHAT I DID TO TAKE CARE OF MYSELF

- walk
- meditate
- bath
- cook

- workout
- yoga
- music
- tv/movie

- read
- pets
- drive
- journal

- family
- friends
- play games
- shopping

- do hobbies
- extra sleep
- favourite food
- _____

- _____
- _____
- _____
- _____

What went well? What made me feel good? What I am proud of?

1. _____
2. _____
3. _____

What contributed to negative emotions? What would I change?

1. _____
2. _____
3. _____

Daily Mood Tracker

DATE: _____

DAY: M – T – W – T – F – S – S

HOURS SLEPT

ENERGY LEVEL

STRESS LEVEL

TODAY I FELT

- loved
- valued
- proud
- grateful

- happy
- joyful
- content
- relaxed

- sick
- tired
- bored
- lazy

- angry
- anxious
- frustrated
- annoyed

- sad
- lonely
- depressed
- insecure

- productive
- motivated
- alive
- excited

- average
- normal
- fine
- OK

THREE THINGS TODAY I AM GRATEFUL FOR

1. _____
2. _____
3. _____

Water Intake (8 Glass A day):

DID I HAVE ENOUGH?   YES   NO

fruits/veggies   ☐   ☐

vitamins   ☐   ☐

fresh air   ☐   ☐

exercise   ☐   ☐

sleep   ☐   ☐

HOW DID I FEEL TODAY IN THE... (CIRCLE ONE)

Morning?

Afternoon?

Evening?

MEDICATIONS

WHAT I DID TO TAKE CARE OF MYSELF

- walk
- meditate
- bath
- cook

- workout
- yoga
- music
- tv/movie

- read
- pets
- drive
- journal

- family
- friends
- play games
- shopping

- do hobbies
- extra sleep
- favourite food
- _____

- _____
- _____
- _____
- _____

What went well? What made me feel good? What I am proud of?

1. _____
2. _____
3. _____

What contributed to negative emotions? What would I change?

1. _____
2. _____
3. _____

Daily Mood Tracker

DATE: _____   DAY: M – T – W – T – F – S – S

HOURS SLEPT	ENERGY LEVEL	STRESS LEVEL

TODAY I FELT

- loved
- valued
- proud
- grateful

- happy
- joyful
- content
- relaxed

- sick
- tired
- bored
- lazy

- angry
- anxious
- frustrated
- annoyed

- sad
- lonely
- depressed
- insecure

- productive
- motivated
- alive
- excited

- average
- normal
- fine
- OK

THREE THINGS TODAY I AM GRATEFUL FOR

1. _____
2. _____
3. _____

Water Intake (8 Glass A day):

DID I HAVE ENOUGH?   YES   NO

fruits/veggies   ☐   ☐

vitamins   ☐   ☐

fresh air   ☐   ☐

exercise   ☐   ☐

sleep   ☐   ☐

HOW DID I FEEL TODAY IN THE... (CIRCLE ONE)

Morning?

Afternoon?

Evening?

MEDICATIONS

WHAT I DID TO TAKE CARE OF MYSELF

- walk
- meditate
- bath
- cook

- workout
- yoga
- music
- tv/movie

- read
- pets
- drive
- journal

- family
- friends
- play games
- shopping

- do hobbies
- extra sleep
- favourite food
- _____

- _____
- _____
- _____
- _____

What went well? What made me feel good? What I am proud of?

1. _____
2. _____
3. _____

What contributed to negative emotions? What would I change?

1. _____
2. _____
3. _____

Daily Mood Tracker

DATE: _____   DAY: M - T - W - T - F - S - S

HOURS SLEPT	ENERGY LEVEL	STRESS LEVEL

TODAY I FELT

- loved
- valued
- proud
- grateful

- happy
- joyful
- content
- relaxed

- sick
- tired
- bored
- lazy

- angry
- anxious
- frustrated
- annoyed

- sad
- lonely
- depressed
- insecure

- productive
- motivated
- alive
- excited

- average
- normal
- fine
- OK

THREE THINGS TODAY I AM GRATEFUL FOR

1. _____
2. _____
3. _____

Water Intake (8 Glass A day):

DID I HAVE ENOUGH?   YES   NO

- fruits/veggies   ☐   ☐
- vitamins   ☐   ☐
- fresh air   ☐   ☐
- exercise   ☐   ☐
- sleep   ☐   ☐

HOW DID I FEEL TODAY IN THE... (CIRCLE ONE)

Morning?

Afternoon?

Evening?

MEDICATIONS

WHAT I DID TO TAKE CARE OF MYSELF

- walk
- meditate
- bath
- cook

- workout
- yoga
- music
- tv/movie

- read
- pets
- drive
- journal

- family
- friends
- play games
- shopping

- do hobbies
- extra sleep
- favourite food
- _____

- _____
- _____
- _____
- _____

What went well? What made me feel good? What I am proud of?

1. _____
2. _____
3. _____

What contributed to negative emotions? What would I change?

1. _____
2. _____
3. _____

Daily Mood Tracker

DATE: _____

DAY: M – T – W – T – F – S – S

HOURS SLEPT	ENERGY LEVEL	STRESS LEVEL

TODAY I FELT

• loved	• happy	• sick	• angry	• sad	• productive	• average
• valued	• joyful	• tired	• anxious	• lonely	• motivated	• normal
• proud	• content	• bored	• frustrated	• depressed	• alive	• fine
• grateful	• relaxed	• lazy	• annoyed	• insecure	• excited	• OK

THREE THINGS TODAY I AM GRATEFUL FOR

1. _____
2. _____
3. _____

Water Intake (8 Glass A day):

DID I HAVE ENOUGH?   YES   NO

fruits/veggies   ☐   ☐

vitamins   ☐   ☐

fresh air   ☐   ☐

exercise   ☐   ☐

sleep   ☐   ☐

HOW DID I FEEL TODAY IN THE... (CIRCLE ONE)

Morning?

Afternoon?

Evening?

MEDICATIONS

WHAT I DID TO TAKE CARE OF MYSELF

• walk	• workout	• read	• family	• do hobbies	• _____
• meditate	• yoga	• pets	• friends	• extra sleep	• _____
• bath	• music	• drive	• play games	• favourite food	• _____
• cook	• tv/movie	• journal	• shopping	• _____	• _____

What went well? What made me feel good? What I am proud of?

1. _____
2. _____
3. _____

What contributed to negative emotions? What would I change?

1. _____
2. _____
3. _____

Daily Mood Tracker

DATE: _____

DAY: M – T – W – T – F – S – S

HOURS SLEPT	ENERGY LEVEL	STRESS LEVEL

TODAY I FELT

- loved
- valued
- proud
- grateful

- happy
- joyful
- content
- relaxed

- sick
- tired
- bored
- lazy

- angry
- anxious
- frustrated
- annoyed

- sad
- lonely
- depressed
- insecure

- productive
- motivated
- alive
- excited

- average
- normal
- fine
- OK

THREE THINGS TODAY I AM GRATEFUL FOR

1. _____
2. _____
3. _____

Water Intake (8 Glass A day):

HOW DID I FEEL TODAY IN THE... (CIRCLE ONE)

Morning?
Afternoon?
Evening?

DID I HAVE ENOUGH?   YES   NO

fruits/veggies ☐ ☐

vitamins ☐ ☐

fresh air ☐ ☐

exercise ☐ ☐

sleep ☐ ☐

MEDICATIONS

WHAT I DID TO TAKE CARE OF MYSELF

- walk
- meditate
- bath
- cook

- workout
- yoga
- music
- tv/movie

- read
- pets
- drive
- journal

- family
- friends
- play games
- shopping

- do hobbies
- extra sleep
- favourite food
- _____

- _____
- _____
- _____
- _____

What went well? What made me feel good? What I am proud of?

1. _____
2. _____
3. _____

What contributed to negative emotions? What would I change?

1. _____
2. _____
3. _____

Daily Mood Tracker

DATE: _____

DAY: M - T - W - T - F - S - S

HOURS SLEPT	ENERGY LEVEL	STRESS LEVEL

TODAY I FELT

- loved
- valued
- proud
- grateful

- happy
- joyful
- content
- relaxed

- sick
- tired
- bored
- lazy

- angry
- anxious
- frustrated
- annoyed

- sad
- lonely
- depressed
- insecure

- productive
- motivated
- alive
- excited

- average
- normal
- fine
- OK

THREE THINGS TODAY I AM GRATEFUL FOR

1. _____
2. _____
3. _____

Water Intake (8 Glass A day):

DID I HAVE ENOUGH?   YES   NO

fruits/veggies   ☐   ☐

vitamins   ☐   ☐

fresh air   ☐   ☐

exercise   ☐   ☐

sleep   ☐   ☐

HOW DID I FEEL TODAY IN THE... (CIRCLE ONE)

Morning?

Afternoon?

Evening?

MEDICATIONS

WHAT I DID TO TAKE CARE OF MYSELF

- walk
- meditate
- bath
- cook

- workout
- yoga
- music
- tv/movie

- read
- pets
- drive
- journal

- family
- friends
- play games
- shopping

- do hobbies
- extra sleep
- favourite food
- _____

- _____
- _____
- _____
- _____

What went well? What made me feel good? What I am proud of?

1. _____
2. _____
3. _____

What contributed to negative emotions? What would I change?

1. _____
2. _____
3. _____

Daily Mood Tracker

DATE: _____

DAY: M - T - W - T - F - S - S

HOURS SLEPT	ENERGY LEVEL	STRESS LEVEL

TODAY I FELT

- loved
- valued
- proud
- grateful

- happy
- joyful
- content
- relaxed

- sick
- tired
- bored
- lazy

- angry
- anxious
- frustrated
- annoyed

- sad
- lonely
- depressed
- insecure

- productive
- motivated
- alive
- excited

- average
- normal
- fine
- OK

THREE THINGS TODAY I AM GRATEFUL FOR

1. _____
2. _____
3. _____

Water Intake (8 Glass A day):

HOW DID I FEEL TODAY IN THE... (CIRCLE ONE)

Morning?

Afternoon?

Evening?

DID I HAVE ENOUGH?   YES   NO

fruits/veggies ☐ ☐

vitamins ☐ ☐

fresh air ☐ ☐

exercise ☐ ☐

sleep ☐ ☐

MEDICATIONS

WHAT I DID TO TAKE CARE OF MYSELF

- walk
- meditate
- bath
- cook

- workout
- yoga
- music
- tv/movie

- read
- pets
- drive
- journal

- family
- friends
- play games
- shopping

- do hobbies
- extra sleep
- favourite food
- _____

- _____
- _____
- _____
- _____

What went well? What made me feel good? What I am proud of?

1. _____
2. _____
3. _____

What contributed to negative emotions? What would I change?

1. _____
2. _____
3. _____

Daily Mood Tracker

DATE: _____

DAY: M – T – W – T – F – S – S

HOURS SLEPT

ENERGY LEVEL

STRESS LEVEL

TODAY I FELT

- loved
- valued
- proud
- grateful

- happy
- joyful
- content
- relaxed

- sick
- tired
- bored
- lazy

- angry
- anxious
- frustrated
- annoyed

- sad
- lonely
- depressed
- insecure

- productive
- motivated
- alive
- excited

- average
- normal
- fine
- OK

THREE THINGS TODAY I AM GRATEFUL FOR

1. _____
2. _____
3. _____

Water Intake (8 Glass A day):

HOW DID I FEEL TODAY IN THE... (CIRCLE ONE)

Morning?

Afternoon?

Evening?

DID I HAVE ENOUGH?   YES   NO

fruits/veggies ☐ ☐

vitamins ☐ ☐

fresh air ☐ ☐

exercise ☐ ☐

sleep ☐ ☐

MEDICATIONS

WHAT I DID TO TAKE CARE OF MYSELF

- walk
- meditate
- bath
- cook

- workout
- yoga
- music
- tv/movie

- read
- pets
- drive
- journal

- family
- friends
- play games
- shopping

- do hobbies
- extra sleep
- favourite food
- _____

- _____
- _____
- _____
- _____

What went well? What made me feel good? What I am proud of?

1. _____
2. _____
3. _____

What contributed to negative emotions? What would I change?

1. _____
2. _____
3. _____

Daily Mood Tracker

DATE: _____   DAY: M – T – W – T – F – S – S

HOURS SLEPT	ENERGY LEVEL	STRESS LEVEL

TODAY I FELT

- loved
- valued
- proud
- grateful

- happy
- joyful
- content
- relaxed

- sick
- tired
- bored
- lazy

- angry
- anxious
- frustrated
- annoyed

- sad
- lonely
- depressed
- insecure

- productive
- motivated
- alive
- excited

- average
- normal
- fine
- OK

THREE THINGS TODAY I AM GRATEFUL FOR

1. _____
2. _____
3. _____

Water Intake (8 Glass A day):

DID I HAVE ENOUGH?   YES   NO

fruits/veggies   ☐   ☐

vitamins   ☐   ☐

fresh air   ☐   ☐

exercise   ☐   ☐

sleep   ☐   ☐

HOW DID I FEEL TODAY IN THE... (CIRCLE ONE)

Morning?

Afternoon?

Evening?

MEDICATIONS

WHAT I DID TO TAKE CARE OF MYSELF

- walk
- meditate
- bath
- cook

- workout
- yoga
- music
- tv/movie

- read
- pets
- drive
- journal

- family
- friends
- play games
- shopping

- do hobbies
- extra sleep
- favourite food
- _____

- _____
- _____
- _____
- _____

What went well? What made me feel good? What I am proud of?

1. _____
2. _____
3. _____

What contributed to negative emotions? What would I change?

1. _____
2. _____
3. _____

Daily Mood Tracker

DATE: _____

DAY: M – T – W – T – F – S – S

HOURS SLEPT

ENERGY LEVEL

STRESS LEVEL

TODAY I FELT

- loved
- valued
- proud
- grateful

- happy
- joyful
- content
- relaxed

- sick
- tired
- bored
- lazy

- angry
- anxious
- frustrated
- annoyed

- sad
- lonely
- depressed
- insecure

- productive
- motivated
- alive
- excited

- average
- normal
- fine
- OK

THREE THINGS TODAY I AM GRATEFUL FOR

1. _____
2. _____
3. _____

Water Intake (8 Glass A day):

HOW DID I FEEL TODAY IN THE... (CIRCLE ONE)

Morning?

Afternoon?

Evening?

DID I HAVE ENOUGH?   YES   NO

fruits/veggies   ☐   ☐

vitamins   ☐   ☐

fresh air   ☐   ☐

exercise   ☐   ☐

sleep   ☐   ☐

MEDICATIONS

WHAT I DID TO TAKE CARE OF MYSELF

- walk
- meditate
- bath
- cook

- workout
- yoga
- music
- tv/movie

- read
- pets
- drive
- journal

- family
- friends
- play games
- shopping

- do hobbies
- extra sleep
- favourite food
- _____

- _____
- _____
- _____
- _____

What went well? What made me feel good? What I am proud of?

1. _____
2. _____
3. _____

What contributed to negative emotions? What would I change?

1. _____
2. _____
3. _____

Daily Mood Tracker

DATE: _____

DAY: M – T – W – T – F – S – S

HOURS SLEPT	ENERGY LEVEL	STRESS LEVEL

TODAY I FELT

- loved
- valued
- proud
- grateful

- happy
- joyful
- content
- relaxed

- sick
- tired
- bored
- lazy

- angry
- anxious
- frustrated
- annoyed

- sad
- lonely
- depressed
- insecure

- productive
- motivated
- alive
- excited

- average
- normal
- fine
- OK

THREE THINGS TODAY I AM GRATEFUL FOR

1. _____
2. _____
3. _____

Water Intake (8 Glass A day):

HOW DID I FEEL TODAY IN THE... (CIRCLE ONE)

Morning?

Afternoon?

Evening?

DID I HAVE ENOUGH?   YES   NO

fruits/veggies ☐ ☐

vitamins ☐ ☐

fresh air ☐ ☐

exercise ☐ ☐

sleep ☐ ☐

MEDICATIONS

WHAT I DID TO TAKE CARE OF MYSELF

- walk
- meditate
- bath
- cook

- workout
- yoga
- music
- tv/movie

- read
- pets
- drive
- journal

- family
- friends
- play games
- shopping

- do hobbies
- extra sleep
- favourite food
- _____

- _____
- _____
- _____
- _____

What went well? What made me feel good? What I am proud of?

1. _____
2. _____
3. _____

What contributed to negative emotions? What would I change?

1. _____
2. _____
3. _____

Daily Mood Tracker

DATE: _____

DAY: M – T – W – T – F – S – S

HOURS SLEPT

ENERGY LEVEL

STRESS LEVEL

TODAY I FELT

- loved
- valued
- proud
- grateful

- happy
- joyful
- content
- relaxed

- sick
- tired
- bored
- lazy

- angry
- anxious
- frustrated
- annoyed

- sad
- lonely
- depressed
- insecure

- productive
- motivated
- alive
- excited

- average
- normal
- fine
- OK

THREE THINGS TODAY I AM GRATEFUL FOR

1. _____
2. _____
3. _____

Water Intake (8 Glass A day):

HOW DID I FEEL TODAY IN THE... (CIRCLE ONE)

Morning?

Afternoon?

Evening?

DID I HAVE ENOUGH?   YES   NO

fruits/veggies   ☐   ☐

vitamins   ☐   ☐

fresh air   ☐   ☐

exercise   ☐   ☐

sleep   ☐   ☐

MEDICATIONS

WHAT I DID TO TAKE CARE OF MYSELF

- walk
- meditate
- bath
- cook

- workout
- yoga
- music
- tv/movie

- read
- pets
- drive
- journal

- family
- friends
- play games
- shopping

- do hobbies
- extra sleep
- favourite food
- _____

- _____
- _____
- _____
- _____

What went well? What made me feel good? What I am proud of?

1. _____
2. _____
3. _____

What contributed to negative emotions? What would I change?

1. _____
2. _____
3. _____

Daily Mood Tracker

DATE: _____

DAY: M – T – W – T – F – S – S

HOURS SLEPT	ENERGY LEVEL	STRESS LEVEL

TODAY I FELT

- loved
- valued
- proud
- grateful

- happy
- joyful
- content
- relaxed

- sick
- tired
- bored
- lazy

- angry
- anxious
- frustrated
- annoyed

- sad
- lonely
- depressed
- insecure

- productive
- motivated
- alive
- excited

- average
- normal
- fine
- OK

THREE THINGS TODAY I AM GRATEFUL FOR

1. _____
2. _____
3. _____

Water Intake (8 Glass A day):

HOW DID I FEEL TODAY IN THE... (CIRCLE ONE)

Morning?

Afternoon?

Evening?

DID I HAVE ENOUGH?	YES	NO
fruits/veggies	☐	☐
vitamins	☐	☐
fresh air	☐	☐
exercise	☐	☐
sleep	☐	☐

MEDICATIONS

WHAT I DID TO TAKE CARE OF MYSELF

- walk
- meditate
- bath
- cook

- workout
- yoga
- music
- tv/movie

- read
- pets
- drive
- journal

- family
- friends
- play games
- shopping

- do hobbies
- extra sleep
- favourite food
- _____

- _____
- _____
- _____
- _____

What went well? What made me feel good? What I am proud of?

1. _____
2. _____
3. _____

What contributed to negative emotions? What would I change?

1. _____
2. _____
3. _____

Daily Mood Tracker

DATE: _____

DAY: M – T – W – T – F – S – S

HOURS SLEPT

ENERGY LEVEL

STRESS LEVEL

TODAY I FELT

- loved
- valued
- proud
- grateful

- happy
- joyful
- content
- relaxed

- sick
- tired
- bored
- lazy

- angry
- anxious
- frustrated
- annoyed

- sad
- lonely
- depressed
- insecure

- productive
- motivated
- alive
- excited

- average
- normal
- fine
- OK

THREE THINGS TODAY I AM GRATEFUL FOR

1. _____
2. _____
3. _____

Water Intake (8 Glass A day):

HOW DID I FEEL TODAY IN THE... (CIRCLE ONE)

Morning?

Afternoon?

Evening?

DID I HAVE ENOUGH?   YES   NO

fruits/veggies   ☐   ☐

vitamins   ☐   ☐

fresh air   ☐   ☐

exercise   ☐   ☐

sleep   ☐   ☐

MEDICATIONS

WHAT I DID TO TAKE CARE OF MYSELF

- walk
- meditate
- bath
- cook

- workout
- yoga
- music
- tv/movie

- read
- pets
- drive
- journal

- family
- friends
- play games
- shopping

- do hobbies
- extra sleep
- favourite food
- _____

- _____
- _____
- _____
- _____

What went well? What made me feel good? What I am proud of?

1. _____
2. _____
3. _____

What contributed to negative emotions? What would I change?

1. _____
2. _____
3. _____

Daily Mood Tracker

DATE: _____

DAY: M - T - W - T - F - S - S

HOURS SLEPT	ENERGY LEVEL	STRESS LEVEL

TODAY I FELT

- loved
- valued
- proud
- grateful

- happy
- joyful
- content
- relaxed

- sick
- tired
- bored
- lazy

- angry
- anxious
- frustrated
- annoyed

- sad
- lonely
- depressed
- insecure

- productive
- motivated
- alive
- excited

- average
- normal
- fine
- OK

THREE THINGS TODAY I AM GRATEFUL FOR

1. _____
2. _____
3. _____

Water Intake (8 Glass A day):

DID I HAVE ENOUGH?   YES   NO

fruits/veggies   ☐   ☐

vitamins   ☐   ☐

fresh air   ☐   ☐

exercise   ☐   ☐

sleep   ☐   ☐

HOW DID I FEEL TODAY IN THE... (CIRCLE ONE)

Morning?

Afternoon?

Evening?

MEDICATIONS

WHAT I DID TO TAKE CARE OF MYSELF

- walk
- meditate
- bath
- cook

- workout
- yoga
- music
- tv/movie

- read
- pets
- drive
- journal

- family
- friends
- play games
- shopping

- do hobbies
- extra sleep
- favourite food
- _____

- _____
- _____
- _____
- _____

What went well? What made me feel good? What I am proud of?

1. _____
2. _____
3. _____

What contributed to negative emotions? What would I change?

1. _____
2. _____
3. _____

Daily Mood Tracker

DATE: _____

DAY: M - T - W - T - F - S - S

HOURS SLEPT

ENERGY LEVEL

STRESS LEVEL

TODAY I FELT

- loved
- valued
- proud
- grateful

- happy
- joyful
- content
- relaxed

- sick
- tired
- bored
- lazy

- angry
- anxious
- frustrated
- annoyed

- sad
- lonely
- depressed
- insecure

- productive
- motivated
- alive
- excited

- average
- normal
- fine
- OK

THREE THINGS TODAY I AM GRATEFUL FOR

1. _____
2. _____
3. _____

Water Intake (8 Glass A day):

HOW DID I FEEL TODAY IN THE... (CIRCLE ONE)

Morning?

Afternoon?

Evening?

DID I HAVE ENOUGH?   YES   NO

fruits/veggies   ☐   ☐

vitamins   ☐   ☐

fresh air   ☐   ☐

exercise   ☐   ☐

sleep   ☐   ☐

MEDICATIONS

WHAT I DID TO TAKE CARE OF MYSELF

- walk
- meditate
- bath
- cook

- workout
- yoga
- music
- tv/movie

- read
- pets
- drive
- journal

- family
- friends
- play games
- shopping

- do hobbies
- extra sleep
- favourite food
- _____

- _____
- _____
- _____
- _____

What went well? What made me feel good? What I am proud of?

1. _____
2. _____
3. _____

What contributed to negative emotions? What would I change?

1. _____
2. _____
3. _____

Daily Mood Tracker

DATE: _____

DAY: M – T – W – T – F – S – S

HOURS SLEPT	ENERGY LEVEL	STRESS LEVEL

TODAY I FELT

- loved
- valued
- proud
- grateful

- happy
- joyful
- content
- relaxed

- sick
- tired
- bored
- lazy

- angry
- anxious
- frustrated
- annoyed

- sad
- lonely
- depressed
- insecure

- productive
- motivated
- alive
- excited

- average
- normal
- fine
- OK

THREE THINGS TODAY I AM GRATEFUL FOR

1. _____
2. _____
3. _____

Water Intake (8 Glass A day):

HOW DID I FEEL TODAY IN THE... (CIRCLE ONE)

Morning?

Afternoon?

Evening?

DID I HAVE ENOUGH?   YES   NO

fruits/veggies   ☐   ☐

vitamins   ☐   ☐

fresh air   ☐   ☐

exercise   ☐   ☐

sleep   ☐   ☐

MEDICATIONS

WHAT I DID TO TAKE CARE OF MYSELF

- walk
- meditate
- bath
- cook

- workout
- yoga
- music
- tv/movie

- read
- pets
- drive
- journal

- family
- friends
- play games
- shopping

- do hobbies
- extra sleep
- favourite food
- _____

- _____
- _____
- _____
- _____

What went well? What made me feel good? What I am proud of?

1. _____
2. _____
3. _____

What contributed to negative emotions? What would I change?

1. _____
2. _____
3. _____

Daily Mood Tracker

DATE: _____   DAY: M – T – W – T – F – S – S

HOURS SLEPT	ENERGY LEVEL	STRESS LEVEL

TODAY I FELT

- loved
- valued
- proud
- grateful

- happy
- joyful
- content
- relaxed

- sick
- tired
- bored
- lazy

- angry
- anxious
- frustrated
- annoyed

- sad
- lonely
- depressed
- insecure

- productive
- motivated
- alive
- excited

- average
- normal
- fine
- OK

THREE THINGS TODAY I AM GRATEFUL FOR

1. _____
2. _____
3. _____

Water Intake (8 Glass A day):

DID I HAVE ENOUGH?   YES   NO

fruits/veggies   ☐   ☐

vitamins   ☐   ☐

fresh air   ☐   ☐

exercise   ☐   ☐

sleep   ☐   ☐

HOW DID I FEEL TODAY IN THE... (CIRCLE ONE)

Morning?

Afternoon?

Evening?

MEDICATIONS

WHAT I DID TO TAKE CARE OF MYSELF

- walk
- meditate
- bath
- cook

- workout
- yoga
- music
- tv/movie

- read
- pets
- drive
- journal

- family
- friends
- play games
- shopping

- do hobbies
- extra sleep
- favourite food
- _____

- _____
- _____
- _____
- _____

What went well? What made me feel good? What I am proud of?

1. _____
2. _____
3. _____

What contributed to negative emotions? What would I change?

1. _____
2. _____
3. _____

Daily Mood Tracker

DATE: _____

DAY: M – T – W – T – F – S – S

HOURS SLEPT

ENERGY LEVEL

STRESS LEVEL

TODAY I FELT

- loved
- valued
- proud
- grateful

- happy
- joyful
- content
- relaxed

- sick
- tired
- bored
- lazy

- angry
- anxious
- frustrated
- annoyed

- sad
- lonely
- depressed
- insecure

- productive
- motivated
- alive
- excited

- average
- normal
- fine
- OK

THREE THINGS TODAY I AM GRATEFUL FOR

1. _____
2. _____
3. _____

Water Intake (8 Glass A day):

DID I HAVE ENOUGH?   YES   NO

fruits/veggies   ☐   ☐

vitamins   ☐   ☐

fresh air   ☐   ☐

exercise   ☐   ☐

sleep   ☐   ☐

HOW DID I FEEL TODAY IN THE... (CIRCLE ONE)

Morning?

Afternoon?

Evening?

MEDICATIONS

WHAT I DID TO TAKE CARE OF MYSELF

- walk
- meditate
- bath
- cook

- workout
- yoga
- music
- tv/movie

- read
- pets
- drive
- journal

- family
- friends
- play games
- shopping

- do hobbies
- extra sleep
- favourite food
- _____

- _____
- _____
- _____
- _____

What went well? What made me feel good? What I am proud of?

1. _____
2. _____
3. _____

What contributed to negative emotions? What would I change?

1. _____
2. _____
3. _____

Daily Mood Tracker

DATE: _____   DAY: M - T - W - T - F - S - S

HOURS SLEPT

ENERGY LEVEL

STRESS LEVEL

TODAY I FELT

- loved
- valued
- proud
- grateful

- happy
- joyful
- content
- relaxed

- sick
- tired
- bored
- lazy

- angry
- anxious
- frustrated
- annoyed

- sad
- lonely
- depressed
- insecure

- productive
- motivated
- alive
- excited

- average
- normal
- fine
- OK

THREE THINGS TODAY I AM GRATEFUL FOR

1. _____
2. _____
3. _____

Water Intake (8 Glass A day):

HOW DID I FEEL TODAY IN THE... (CIRCLE ONE)

Morning?

Afternoon?

Evening?

DID I HAVE ENOUGH?   YES   NO

fruits/veggies   ☐   ☐

vitamins   ☐   ☐

fresh air   ☐   ☐

exercise   ☐   ☐

sleep   ☐   ☐

MEDICATIONS

WHAT I DID TO TAKE CARE OF MYSELF

- walk
- meditate
- bath
- cook

- workout
- yoga
- music
- tv/movie

- read
- pets
- drive
- journal

- family
- friends
- play games
- shopping

- do hobbies
- extra sleep
- favourite food
- _____

- _____
- _____
- _____
- _____

What went well? What made me feel good? What I am proud of?

1. _____
2. _____
3. _____

What contributed to negative emotions? What would I change?

1. _____
2. _____
3. _____

Daily Mood Tracker

DATE: _____

DAY: M - T - W - T - F - S - S

HOURS SLEPT	ENERGY LEVEL	STRESS LEVEL

TODAY I FELT

- loved
- valued
- proud
- grateful

- happy
- joyful
- content
- relaxed

- sick
- tired
- bored
- lazy

- angry
- anxious
- frustrated
- annoyed

- sad
- lonely
- depressed
- insecure

- productive
- motivated
- alive
- excited

- average
- normal
- fine
- OK

THREE THINGS TODAY I AM GRATEFUL FOR

1. _____
2. _____
3. _____

Water Intake (8 Glass A day):

HOW DID I FEEL TODAY IN THE... (CIRCLE ONE)

Morning?

Afternoon?

Evening?

DID I HAVE ENOUGH?

	YES	NO
fruits/veggies	☐	☐
vitamins	☐	☐
fresh air	☐	☐
exercise	☐	☐
sleep	☐	☐

MEDICATIONS

WHAT I DID TO TAKE CARE OF MYSELF

- walk
- meditate
- bath
- cook

- workout
- yoga
- music
- tv/movie

- read
- pets
- drive
- journal

- family
- friends
- play games
- shopping

- do hobbies
- extra sleep
- favourite food
- _____

- _____
- _____
- _____
- _____

What went well? What made me feel good? What I am proud of?

1. _____
2. _____
3. _____

What contributed to negative emotions? What would I change?

1. _____
2. _____
3. _____

Daily Mood Tracker

DATE: _____

DAY: M – T – W – T – F – S – S

HOURS SLEPT

ENERGY LEVEL

STRESS LEVEL

TODAY I FELT

- loved
- valued
- proud
- grateful

- happy
- joyful
- content
- relaxed

- sick
- tired
- bored
- lazy

- angry
- anxious
- frustrated
- annoyed

- sad
- lonely
- depressed
- insecure

- productive
- motivated
- alive
- excited

- average
- normal
- fine
- OK

THREE THINGS TODAY I AM GRATEFUL FOR

1. _____
2. _____
3. _____

Water Intake (8 Glass A day):

HOW DID I FEEL TODAY IN THE... (CIRCLE ONE)

Morning?

Afternoon?

Evening?

DID I HAVE ENOUGH?   YES   NO

fruits/veggies ☐ ☐

vitamins ☐ ☐

fresh air ☐ ☐

exercise ☐ ☐

sleep ☐ ☐

MEDICATIONS

WHAT I DID TO TAKE CARE OF MYSELF

- walk
- meditate
- bath
- cook

- workout
- yoga
- music
- tv/movie

- read
- pets
- drive
- journal

- family
- friends
- play games
- shopping

- do hobbies
- extra sleep
- favourite food
- _____

- _ _ _ _ _ _ _ _
- _ _ _ _ _ _ _ _
- _ _ _ _ _ _ _ _
- _ _ _ _ _ _ _ _

What went well? What made me feel good? What I am proud of?

1. _____
2. _____
3. _____

What contributed to negative emotions? What would I change?

1. _____
2. _____
3. _____

Daily Mood Tracker

DATE: _____

DAY: M - T - W - T - F - S - S

HOURS SLEPT

ENERGY LEVEL

STRESS LEVEL

TODAY I FELT

- loved
- valued
- proud
- grateful

- happy
- joyful
- content
- relaxed

- sick
- tired
- bored
- lazy

- angry
- anxious
- frustrated
- annoyed

- sad
- lonely
- depressed
- insecure

- productive
- motivated
- alive
- excited

- average
- normal
- fine
- OK

THREE THINGS TODAY I AM GRATEFUL FOR

1. _____
2. _____
3. _____

Water Intake (8 Glass A day):

DID I HAVE ENOUGH?

	YES	NO
fruits/veggies	☐	☐
vitamins	☐	☐
fresh air	☐	☐
exercise	☐	☐
sleep	☐	☐

HOW DID I FEEL TODAY IN THE... (CIRCLE ONE)

Morning?

Afternoon?

Evening?

MEDICATIONS

WHAT I DID TO TAKE CARE OF MYSELF

- walk
- meditate
- bath
- cook

- workout
- yoga
- music
- tv/movie

- read
- pets
- drive
- journal

- family
- friends
- play games
- shopping

- do hobbies
- extra sleep
- favourite food
- _____

- _____
- _____
- _____
- _____

What went well? What made me feel good? What I am proud of?

1. _____
2. _____
3. _____

What contributed to negative emotions? What would I change?

1. _____
2. _____
3. _____

Daily Mood Tracker

DATE: _____

DAY: M – T – W – T – F – S – S

HOURS SLEPT

ENERGY LEVEL

STRESS LEVEL

TODAY I FELT

- loved
- valued
- proud
- grateful

- happy
- joyful
- content
- relaxed

- sick
- tired
- bored
- lazy

- angry
- anxious
- frustrated
- annoyed

- sad
- lonely
- depressed
- insecure

- productive
- motivated
- alive
- excited

- average
- normal
- fine
- OK

THREE THINGS TODAY I AM GRATEFUL FOR

1. _____
2. _____
3. _____

Water Intake (8 Glass A day):

HOW DID I FEEL TODAY IN THE... (CIRCLE ONE)

Morning?

Afternoon?

Evening?

DID I HAVE ENOUGH?   YES   NO

fruits/veggies   ☐   ☐

vitamins   ☐   ☐

fresh air   ☐   ☐

exercise   ☐   ☐

sleep   ☐   ☐

MEDICATIONS

WHAT I DID TO TAKE CARE OF MYSELF

- walk
- meditate
- bath
- cook

- workout
- yoga
- music
- tv/movie

- read
- pets
- drive
- journal

- family
- friends
- play games
- shopping

- do hobbies
- extra sleep
- favourite food
- _____

- _____
- _____
- _____
- _____

What went well? What made me feel good? What I am proud of?

1. _____
2. _____
3. _____

What contributed to negative emotions? What would I change?

1. _____
2. _____
3. _____

Daily Mood Tracker

DATE: _____

DAY: M – T – W – T – F – S – S

HOURS SLEPT

ENERGY LEVEL

STRESS LEVEL

TODAY I FELT

- loved
- valued
- proud
- grateful

- happy
- joyful
- content
- relaxed

- sick
- tired
- bored
- lazy

- angry
- anxious
- frustrated
- annoyed

- sad
- lonely
- depressed
- insecure

- productive
- motivated
- alive
- excited

- average
- normal
- fine
- OK

THREE THINGS TODAY I AM GRATEFUL FOR

1. _____
2. _____
3. _____

Water Intake (8 Glass A day):

DID I HAVE ENOUGH?   YES   NO

fruits/veggies   ☐   ☐

vitamins   ☐   ☐

fresh air   ☐   ☐

exercise   ☐   ☐

sleep   ☐   ☐

HOW DID I FEEL TODAY IN THE... (CIRCLE ONE)

Morning?

Afternoon?

Evening?

MEDICATIONS

WHAT I DID TO TAKE CARE OF MYSELF

- walk
- meditate
- bath
- cook

- workout
- yoga
- music
- tv/movie

- read
- pets
- drive
- journal

- family
- friends
- play games
- shopping

- do hobbies
- extra sleep
- favourite food
- _____

- _____
- _____
- _____
- _____

What went well? What made me feel good? What I am proud of?

1. _____
2. _____
3. _____

What contributed to negative emotions? What would I change?

1. _____
2. _____
3. _____

Daily Mood Tracker

DATE: _____

DAY: M – T – W – T – F – S – S

HOURS SLEPT	ENERGY LEVEL	STRESS LEVEL

TODAY I FELT

- loved
- valued
- proud
- grateful

- happy
- joyful
- content
- relaxed

- sick
- tired
- bored
- lazy

- angry
- anxious
- frustrated
- annoyed

- sad
- lonely
- depressed
- insecure

- productive
- motivated
- alive
- excited

- average
- normal
- fine
- OK

THREE THINGS TODAY I AM GRATEFUL FOR

1. _____
2. _____
3. _____

Water Intake (8 Glass A day):

HOW DID I FEEL TODAY IN THE... (CIRCLE ONE)

Morning?

Afternoon?

Evening?

DID I HAVE ENOUGH?	YES	NO
fruits/veggies	☐	☐
vitamins	☐	☐
fresh air	☐	☐
exercise	☐	☐
sleep	☐	☐

MEDICATIONS

WHAT I DID TO TAKE CARE OF MYSELF

- walk
- meditate
- bath
- cook

- workout
- yoga
- music
- tv/movie

- read
- pets
- drive
- journal

- family
- friends
- play games
- shopping

- do hobbies
- extra sleep
- favourite food
- _____

- _____
- _____
- _____
- _____

What went well? What made me feel good? What I am proud of?

1. _____
2. _____
3. _____

What contributed to negative emotions? What would I change?

1. _____
2. _____
3. _____

Daily Mood Tracker

DATE: _____

DAY: M - T - W - T - F - S - S

HOURS SLEPT

ENERGY LEVEL

STRESS LEVEL

TODAY I FELT

- loved
- valued
- proud
- grateful

- happy
- joyful
- content
- relaxed

- sick
- tired
- bored
- lazy

- angry
- anxious
- frustrated
- annoyed

- sad
- lonely
- depressed
- insecure

- productive
- motivated
- alive
- excited

- average
- normal
- fine
- OK

THREE THINGS TODAY I AM GRATEFUL FOR

1. _____
2. _____
3. _____

Water Intake (8 Glass A day):

DID I HAVE ENOUGH?   YES   NO

fruits/veggies   ☐   ☐

vitamins   ☐   ☐

fresh air   ☐   ☐

exercise   ☐   ☐

sleep   ☐   ☐

HOW DID I FEEL TODAY IN THE... (CIRCLE ONE)

Morning?

Afternoon?

Evening?

MEDICATIONS

WHAT I DID TO TAKE CARE OF MYSELF

- walk
- meditate
- bath
- cook

- workout
- yoga
- music
- tv/movie

- read
- pets
- drive
- journal

- family
- friends
- play games
- shopping

- do hobbies
- extra sleep
- favourite food
- _____

- _____
- _____
- _____
- _____

What went well? What made me feel good? What I am proud of?

1. _____
2. _____
3. _____

What contributed to negative emotions? What would I change?

1. _____
2. _____
3. _____

Daily Mood Tracker

DATE: _____

DAY: M – T – W – T – F – S – S

HOURS SLEPT

ENERGY LEVEL

STRESS LEVEL

TODAY I FELT

- loved
- valued
- proud
- grateful

- happy
- joyful
- content
- relaxed

- sick
- tired
- bored
- lazy

- angry
- anxious
- frustrated
- annoyed

- sad
- lonely
- depressed
- insecure

- productive
- motivated
- alive
- excited

- average
- normal
- fine
- OK

THREE THINGS TODAY I AM GRATEFUL FOR

1. _____
2. _____
3. _____

Water Intake (8 Glass A day):

HOW DID I FEEL TODAY IN THE... (CIRCLE ONE)

Morning?

Afternoon?

Evening?

DID I HAVE ENOUGH?   YES   NO

fruits/veggies   ☐   ☐

vitamins   ☐   ☐

fresh air   ☐   ☐

exercise   ☐   ☐

sleep   ☐   ☐

MEDICATIONS

WHAT I DID TO TAKE CARE OF MYSELF

- walk
- meditate
- bath
- cook

- workout
- yoga
- music
- tv/movie

- read
- pets
- drive
- journal

- family
- friends
- play games
- shopping

- do hobbies
- extra sleep
- favourite food
- _____

- _____
- _____
- _____
- _____

What went well? What made me feel good? What I am proud of?

1. _____
2. _____
3. _____

What contributed to negative emotions? What would I change?

1. _____
2. _____
3. _____

Daily Mood Tracker

DATE: _____

DAY: M – T – W – T – F – S – S

HOURS SLEPT	ENERGY LEVEL	STRESS LEVEL

TODAY I FELT

- loved
- valued
- proud
- grateful

- happy
- joyful
- content
- relaxed

- sick
- tired
- bored
- lazy

- angry
- anxious
- frustrated
- annoyed

- sad
- lonely
- depressed
- insecure

- productive
- motivated
- alive
- excited

- average
- normal
- fine
- OK

THREE THINGS TODAY I AM GRATEFUL FOR

1. _____
2. _____
3. _____

Water Intake (8 Glass A day):

DID I HAVE ENOUGH?   YES   NO

fruits/veggies   ☐   ☐

vitamins   ☐   ☐

fresh air   ☐   ☐

exercise   ☐   ☐

sleep   ☐   ☐

HOW DID I FEEL TODAY IN THE... (CIRCLE ONE)

Morning?

Afternoon?

Evening?

MEDICATIONS

WHAT I DID TO TAKE CARE OF MYSELF

- walk
- meditate
- bath
- cook

- workout
- yoga
- music
- tv/movie

- read
- pets
- drive
- journal

- family
- friends
- play games
- shopping

- do hobbies
- extra sleep
- favourite food
- _____

- _____
- _____
- _____
- _____

What went well? What made me feel good? What I am proud of?

1. _____
2. _____
3. _____

What contributed to negative emotions? What would I change?

1. _____
2. _____
3. _____

Daily Mood Tracker

DATE: _____   DAY: M – T – W – T – F – S – S

HOURS SLEPT

ENERGY LEVEL

STRESS LEVEL

TODAY I FELT

- loved
- valued
- proud
- grateful

- happy
- joyful
- content
- relaxed

- sick
- tired
- bored
- lazy

- angry
- anxious
- frustrated
- annoyed

- sad
- lonely
- depressed
- insecure

- productive
- motivated
- alive
- excited

- average
- normal
- fine
- OK

THREE THINGS TODAY I AM GRATEFUL FOR

1. _____
2. _____
3. _____

Water Intake (8 Glass A day):

DID I HAVE ENOUGH?   YES   NO

fruits/veggies   ☐   ☐

vitamins   ☐   ☐

fresh air   ☐   ☐

exercise   ☐   ☐

sleep   ☐   ☐

HOW DID I FEEL TODAY IN THE... (CIRCLE ONE)

Morning?

Afternoon?

Evening?

MEDICATIONS

WHAT I DID TO TAKE CARE OF MYSELF

- walk
- meditate
- bath
- cook

- workout
- yoga
- music
- tv/movie

- read
- pets
- drive
- journal

- family
- friends
- play games
- shopping

- do hobbies
- extra sleep
- favourite food
- _____

- _____
- _____
- _____
- _____

What went well? What made me feel good? What I am proud of?

1. _____
2. _____
3. _____

What contributed to negative emotions? What would I change?

1. _____
2. _____
3. _____

Daily Mood Tracker

DATE: _____

DAY: M – T – W – T – F – S – S

HOURS SLEPT	ENERGY LEVEL	STRESS LEVEL

TODAY I FELT

- loved
- valued
- proud
- grateful

- happy
- joyful
- content
- relaxed

- sick
- tired
- bored
- lazy

- angry
- anxious
- frustrated
- annoyed

- sad
- lonely
- depressed
- insecure

- productive
- motivated
- alive
- excited

- average
- normal
- fine
- OK

THREE THINGS TODAY I AM GRATEFUL FOR

1. _____
2. _____
3. _____

Water Intake (8 Glass A day):

HOW DID I FEEL TODAY IN THE... (CIRCLE ONE)

Morning?

Afternoon?

Evening?

DID I HAVE ENOUGH?

	YES	NO
fruits/veggies	☐	☐
vitamins	☐	☐
fresh air	☐	☐
exercise	☐	☐
sleep	☐	☐

MEDICATIONS

WHAT I DID TO TAKE CARE OF MYSELF

- walk
- meditate
- bath
- cook

- workout
- yoga
- music
- tv/movie

- read
- pets
- drive
- journal

- family
- friends
- play games
- shopping

- do hobbies
- extra sleep
- favourite food
- _____

- _____
- _____
- _____
- _____

What went well? What made me feel good? What I am proud of?

1. _____
2. _____
3. _____

What contributed to negative emotions? What would I change?

1. _____
2. _____
3. _____

Daily Mood Tracker

DATE: _____

DAY: M – T – W – T – F – S – S

HOURS SLEPT

ENERGY LEVEL

STRESS LEVEL

TODAY I FELT

- loved
- valued
- proud
- grateful

- happy
- joyful
- content
- relaxed

- sick
- tired
- bored
- lazy

- angry
- anxious
- frustrated
- annoyed

- sad
- lonely
- depressed
- insecure

- productive
- motivated
- alive
- excited

- average
- normal
- fine
- OK

THREE THINGS TODAY I AM GRATEFUL FOR

1. _____
2. _____
3. _____

Water Intake (8 Glass A day):

HOW DID I FEEL TODAY IN THE... (CIRCLE ONE)

Morning?

Afternoon?

Evening?

DID I HAVE ENOUGH?   YES   NO

fruits/veggies

vitamins

fresh air

exercise

sleep

MEDICATIONS

WHAT I DID TO TAKE CARE OF MYSELF

- walk
- meditate
- bath
- cook

- workout
- yoga
- music
- tv/movie

- read
- pets
- drive
- journal

- family
- friends
- play games
- shopping

- do hobbies
- extra sleep
- favourite food
- _____

- _____
- _____
- _____
- _____

What went well? What made me feel good? What I am proud of?

1. _____
2. _____
3. _____

What contributed to negative emotions? What would I change?

1. _____
2. _____
3. _____

Daily Mood Tracker

DATE: _____

DAY: M – T – W – T – F – S – S

HOURS SLEPT

ENERGY LEVEL

STRESS LEVEL

TODAY I FELT

- loved
- valued
- proud
- grateful

- happy
- joyful
- content
- relaxed

- sick
- tired
- bored
- lazy

- angry
- anxious
- frustrated
- annoyed

- sad
- lonely
- depressed
- insecure

- productive
- motivated
- alive
- excited

- average
- normal
- fine
- OK

THREE THINGS TODAY I AM GRATEFUL FOR

1. _____
2. _____
3. _____

Water Intake (8 Glass A day):

HOW DID I FEEL TODAY IN THE... (CIRCLE ONE)

Morning?

Afternoon?

Evening?

DID I HAVE ENOUGH?   YES   NO

fruits/veggies   ☐   ☐

vitamins   ☐   ☐

fresh air   ☐   ☐

exercise   ☐   ☐

sleep   ☐   ☐

MEDICATIONS

WHAT I DID TO TAKE CARE OF MYSELF

- walk
- meditate
- bath
- cook

- workout
- yoga
- music
- tv/movie

- read
- pets
- drive
- journal

- family
- friends
- play games
- shopping

- do hobbies
- extra sleep
- favourite food
- _____

- _____
- _____
- _____
- _____

What went well? What made me feel good? What I am proud of?

1. _____
2. _____
3. _____

What contributed to negative emotions? What would I change?

1. _____
2. _____
3. _____

Daily Mood Tracker

DATE: _____

DAY: M – T – W – T – F – S – S

HOURS SLEPT

ENERGY LEVEL

STRESS LEVEL

TODAY I FELT

- loved
- valued
- proud
- grateful

- happy
- joyful
- content
- relaxed

- sick
- tired
- bored
- lazy

- angry
- anxious
- frustrated
- annoyed

- sad
- lonely
- depressed
- insecure

- productive
- motivated
- alive
- excited

- average
- normal
- fine
- OK

THREE THINGS TODAY I AM GRATEFUL FOR

1. _____
2. _____
3. _____

Water Intake (8 Glass A day):

HOW DID I FEEL TODAY IN THE... (CIRCLE ONE)

Morning?

Afternoon?

Evening?

DID I HAVE ENOUGH?   YES   NO

fruits/veggies   ☐   ☐

vitamins   ☐   ☐

fresh air   ☐   ☐

exercise   ☐   ☐

sleep   ☐   ☐

MEDICATIONS

WHAT I DID TO TAKE CARE OF MYSELF

- walk
- meditate
- bath
- cook

- workout
- yoga
- music
- tv/movie

- read
- pets
- drive
- journal

- family
- friends
- play games
- shopping

- do hobbies
- extra sleep
- favourite food
- _____

- _____
- _____
- _____
- _____

What went well? What made me feel good? What I am proud of?

1. _____
2. _____
3. _____

What contributed to negative emotions? What would I change?

1. _____
2. _____
3. _____

Daily Mood Tracker

DATE: _____

DAY: M – T – W – T – F – S – S

HOURS SLEPT	ENERGY LEVEL	STRESS LEVEL

TODAY I FELT

- loved
- valued
- proud
- grateful

- happy
- joyful
- content
- relaxed

- sick
- tired
- bored
- lazy

- angry
- anxious
- frustrated
- annoyed

- sad
- lonely
- depressed
- insecure

- productive
- motivated
- alive
- excited

- average
- normal
- fine
- OK

THREE THINGS TODAY I AM GRATEFUL FOR

1. _____
2. _____
3. _____

Water Intake (8 Glass A day):

DID I HAVE ENOUGH?   YES   NO

fruits/veggies   ☐   ☐

vitamins   ☐   ☐

fresh air   ☐   ☐

exercise   ☐   ☐

sleep   ☐   ☐

HOW DID I FEEL TODAY IN THE... (CIRCLE ONE)

Morning?

Afternoon?

Evening?

MEDICATIONS

WHAT I DID TO TAKE CARE OF MYSELF

- walk
- meditate
- bath
- cook

- workout
- yoga
- music
- tv/movie

- read
- pets
- drive
- journal

- family
- friends
- play games
- shopping

- do hobbies
- extra sleep
- favourite food
- _____

- _____
- _____
- _____
- _____

What went well? What made me feel good? What I am proud of?

1. _____
2. _____
3. _____

What contributed to negative emotions? What would I change?

1. _____
2. _____
3. _____

Daily Mood Tracker

DATE: _____

DAY: M – T – W – T – F – S – S

HOURS SLEPT	ENERGY LEVEL	STRESS LEVEL

TODAY I FELT

- loved
- valued
- proud
- grateful

- happy
- joyful
- content
- relaxed

- sick
- tired
- bored
- lazy

- angry
- anxious
- frustrated
- annoyed

- sad
- lonely
- depressed
- insecure

- productive
- motivated
- alive
- excited

- average
- normal
- fine
- OK

THREE THINGS TODAY I AM GRATEFUL FOR

1. _____
2. _____
3. _____

Water Intake (8 Glass A day):

DID I HAVE ENOUGH?   YES   NO

fruits/veggies ☐ ☐

vitamins ☐ ☐

fresh air ☐ ☐

exercise ☐ ☐

sleep ☐ ☐

HOW DID I FEEL TODAY IN THE... (CIRCLE ONE)

Morning?

Afternoon?

Evening?

MEDICATIONS

WHAT I DID TO TAKE CARE OF MYSELF

- walk
- meditate
- bath
- cook

- workout
- yoga
- music
- tv/movie

- read
- pets
- drive
- journal

- family
- friends
- play games
- shopping

- do hobbies
- extra sleep
- favourite food
- _____

- _____
- _____
- _____
- _____

What went well? What made me feel good? What I am proud of?

1. _____
2. _____
3. _____

What contributed to negative emotions? What would I change?

1. _____
2. _____
3. _____

Daily Mood Tracker

DATE: _____

DAY: M – T – W – T – F – S – S

HOURS SLEPT	ENERGY LEVEL	STRESS LEVEL

TODAY I FELT

- loved
- valued
- proud
- grateful

- happy
- joyful
- content
- relaxed

- sick
- tired
- bored
- lazy

- angry
- anxious
- frustrated
- annoyed

- sad
- lonely
- depressed
- insecure

- productive
- motivated
- alive
- excited

- average
- normal
- fine
- OK

THREE THINGS TODAY I AM GRATEFUL FOR

1. _____
2. _____
3. _____

Water Intake (8 Glass A day):

DID I HAVE ENOUGH?   YES   NO

- fruits/veggies   ☐   ☐
- vitamins   ☐   ☐
- fresh air   ☐   ☐
- exercise   ☐   ☐
- sleep   ☐   ☐

HOW DID I FEEL TODAY IN THE... (CIRCLE ONE)

Morning?

Afternoon?

Evening?

MEDICATIONS

WHAT I DID TO TAKE CARE OF MYSELF

- walk
- meditate
- bath
- cook

- workout
- yoga
- music
- tv/movie

- read
- pets
- drive
- journal

- family
- friends
- play games
- shopping

- do hobbies
- extra sleep
- favourite food
- _____

- _____
- _____
- _____
- _____

What went well? What made me feel good? What I am proud of?

1. _____
2. _____
3. _____

What contributed to negative emotions? What would I change?

1. _____
2. _____
3. _____

Made in United States
North Haven, CT
09 June 2023

37551452R00063